A PSYCHIATRIST
LOOKS AT
RELIGION AND HEALTH

A PSYCHIATRIST
LOOKS AT
RELIGION AND HEALTH

JAMES A. KNIGHT

✠

☥

ABINGDON PRESS / NEW YORK / NASHVILLE

A PSYCHIATRIST LOOKS AT RELIGION AND HEALTH

Copyright © 1964 by Abingdon Press

Library of Congress Catalog Card Number: 64-21132

Acknowledgment is made to the following journals in which several chapters of this book have previously been published: *Mental Hygiene* for "Spiritual Concerns and Mental Health"; *The Journal of Existential Psychiatry* for "Carl Gustav Jung: Religious and Psychological Concerns"; *Pastoral Psychology* for "Freud and Calvin: A Comparative Study" and "The Use and Misuse of Religion by the Emotionally Disturbed"; and *Psychosomatic Medicine* for "False Pregnancy in a Male."

SET UP, PRINTED, AND BOUND BY THE PARTHENON PRESS, AT NASHVILLE, TENNESSEE, UNITED STATES OF AMERICA

Dedicated
to the memory of
my parents,
Thomas Samuel Knight
and
Carolyn Carn Knight

PREFACE

The student of human behavior, whether he be psychiatrist or clergyman, is confronted daily with problems relating to the philosophical and religious concerns of the individual. Between these two disciplines there is much overlapping of thought, yet there are often vast professional differences in the handling of problems and in the approach to their resolution. Out of a half-century of conflict there is gradually emerging a spirit of cooperation and an appreciation of what each has to contribute to the enigmatic nature of the human spirit.

During World War II, I served as the chaplain of a U.S. Navy hospital ship which operated in the Pacific theater. One major responsibility was counseling the crew members and dealing with the numerous problems of the sick, wounded, and dying. Many of the problems brought to the chaplain were easy to

7

handle, but others were extremely complicated with determinants which seemed to be hidden or, at least, elusive. When I discussed this situation with several of the physicians who were serving aboard this ship, they pointed out the difficulty, even in the best of circumstances, of seeing all the facets of a problem or of comprehending many of the motivating factors behind human behavior. They mentioned the limitation in the average clergyman's training in this area. If one were truly interested in the field of counseling and psychotherapy, then it would be necessary for him to take further training. They recommended training in clinical psychology or going to medical school and, after graduation, specializing in psychiatry.

I was so challenged by the possibility of working in both fields—psychiatry and religion—that I soon made the decision to combine my theological training with that of medicine and psychiatry. Since completing my psychiatric specialty training I have maintained a major interest in the interaction of psychiatry and religion, and have endeavored to develop a subspecialty in this particular field.

The journey through medical and psychiatric training was an inspirational and enriching experience. Whether looking at brain tissue under the microscope or probing deep into the unconscious mind of a patient I found there the hand of God in a way that became clearer and more real every day.

Medicine and religion have shared many of the same ideals and spiritual values. Society understands the clergyman's vocation as a spiritual calling. Its view of the physician's work is somewhat similar.

The physician has a mission or calling with a core that tends toward the sacred, that even may be sacred. It is the misfortune of our medical profession that this very core may have been lost in the materialism of our era. Yet the cynical materialism of today should not be allowed to engulf medicine.

There should be no conflict between religion and medicine. The physician must be a man of science when facing disease and a man of faith when facing the patient. Before the facts he is a scientist, and before his fellowman he is a religious person. Healing is a sacred act requiring clean hands and a pure heart. The physician should cultivate the relationship of faith with the patient, for in this faith resides the key to the healing miracle. The physician's voice and hands and the patient's faith are the things that ultimately direct the healing drug, the mending scalpel, or the reassuring psychotherapy. Such a spiritual legacy was bequeathed to us by Luke, who besides being a good man was called the "beloved physician."

The physician has often had to face the conflict between his pragmatic education and his spiritual inclination to feel religious awe, as he faces the marvels of the human body and mind. Throughout its long history medicine has at times soared vertically in search of God and at other times spread horizontally to explore the nature of man. Medicine's greatest conquest in the future will not be in the conquest of cosmic outer space nor that of man's physical and mental inner space but in aiding the renaissance of love and service for man. The prescription for love and service was set forth more than two thousand years ago by the venerable Greek physician, Hippocrates, in his oath of ethics and morals. This is still the physician's best guide for the space age, as he becomes an excellent ambassador of good will among men, of health, and of peace on earth.

This book is addressed not to a restricted audience but a broad group of readers. I have thought of clergymen and interested laymen. My colleagues in psychiatry and general medicine will find many of their concerns discussed. Topics dealing with psychiatry and religion touch our lives and work at vital points. Those who work with people or have an interest in human behavior can no longer avoid involvement in the crucial issues, where the domains of psychiatry and religion overlap. The question today is how well will we deal with these issues, and how great will be our understanding.

When one writes on the topic of psychiatry and religion, he is indebted to a host of authorities of the past and present, too numerous to mention.

In this book I have drawn some upon papers which I previously published in journals. In most instances this material has been

9

revised considerably. For permission to use, in revised form, this previously published material I am indebted to the editors and publishers of *Mental Hygiene, Pastoral Psychology, Psychiatric Quarterly, Psychosomatic Medicine,* and *The Journal of Existential Psychiatry.*

I am also indebted to Mrs. Barbara Kerr, executive secretary, Program in Psychiatry and Religion, Union Theological Seminary, who rendered excellent editorial assistance. Mrs. Isabel Letts performed much-needed secretarial help. My wife assisted with many of the editorial and secretarial tasks associated with the project and was a constant source of encouragement and challenge.

JAMES A. KNIGHT

CONTENTS

I

MAN'S CAPACITY AND QUEST FOR HEALTH

1

The Body's Miraculous Wisdom

Our thoughts are turned daily toward the processes of renewal inherent in all living matter. The capacity of all living matter to renew itself gives us all abundant material for meditation and spiritual searching.

Any physician who pauses momentarily can remember vividly a wide variety of acute surgical and medical emergencies he has treated. Many of these people came close to death—yet they lived. These experiences are graphic portrayals of the body's victory over disease and injury. One cannot help being repeatedly impressed with the persistence of life, the body's unwillingness to accept defeat and death. Every time I am in a hospital's emergency room I witness again this capacity of the human organism.

Each disturbing influence in these patients has induced by itself the calling forth of compensatory activities to neutralize or repair the disturbance. In contemplation of these factors one can readily agree with the wisdom exhibited by the psalmist when he sang: "For I am fearfully and wonderfully made: marvellous are thy works" (Ps. 139:14).

The human machine operates for a limited period of time. Biblically it is given three score years and ten. Its parts are susceptible to constant wear and tear, and also to damage which may seriously impair the function of the whole organism. No tissue or organ in the body is exempt from this. Success in the struggle for physical existence depends in a large measure upon the evolution of mechanisms which weight the balance between health and disease in favor of health.

Some of the same mechanisms which are always functioning in the normal person also operate as defensive mechanisms in disease and injury. Actually, all physiological mechanisms con-

15

stitute defenses against disease, for they function to preserve a constancy in the internal environment, which, if changed appreciably, spell disease and death. Claud Bernard, the famous French physiologist, said: "All the vital mechanisms, however varied they may be, have only one object, that of preserving constant the conditions of life."

Human beings are composed of materials in the body's structure which are characterized by the utmost inconstancy and instability. Yet the body has learned methods of maintaining constancy and steadiness in the presence of conditions which are threatening and profoundly disturbing. This ability of living beings to maintain their constancy is called homeostasis and has always impressed biologists and physicians.

The concept that disease is cured by natural powers, by a *vis medicatrix naturae*, was held by many of the ancient great physicians, including Hippocrates (460-377 B.C.). This idea implies the existence of forces which are ready to operate correctively when the normal state of the organism is upset. The acceptance of this concept was an honest recognition by these physicians that processes of repair after injury, and of restoration to health after sickness, go on independently of any treatment by a physician. Thus, in an awe-inspiring fashion, the normal state of the organism is maintained or its disturbed balance reestablished by automatic physiological reactions. The sick or injured should seldom be without hope, for in his body there are admirable devices for maintaining its stability against threatening internal and external conditions. The powers of healing and the margin of safety of human physiology are so great that they stagger the imagination. A prominent scientist once said, "I do not wonder that people die; that is easy enough. What I marvel at is that they go on living with bodies so maimed, disordered, and worn out."

Nature's great abundance to our bodies can be illustrated in many ways. There are many paired organs in the body, such as the kidneys, adrenal glands, and lungs. Only one of the paired organs is needed for the continued existence and efficiency of the body. With one kidney gone the amount and composition of

16

the urinary secretion is practically unchanged. If both adrenal glands are excised, death follows usually within thirty-six hours. However, if one tenth of the adrenal tissue is left, the existence of the organism is not jeopardized. Only one fifth of the thyroid tissue is required to prevent myxedema—a disease characterized by puffiness of the face and hands, slowing of the pulse rate, dryness and wrinkling of the skin, falling of the hair, dulling of mental activity, sluggishness of movement, and lowering of the basal metabolic rate. The four small parathyroid glands are essential in maintaining the proper calcium and phosphorus concentration in the blood. Their removal results in muscular tremors, convulsions, coma, and death, unless the parathyroid hormones are supplied by medication. Elimination of two of the glands is not followed by any disturbance in metabolism.

The safety factors in unpaired organs are more striking than in the paired. The pancreas produces insulin, which is required for the utilization of carbohydrates by the organism. Removal of the pancreas causes severe diabetes mellitus. Yet four fifths of the organ can be removed without ill effect. Thus, only one fifth of the pancreas is required to produce the insulin needed. The liver is the hub organ of the body, with a multitude of important functions. It plays a significant role in the metabolism of proteins, carbohydrates, and fats. It detoxifies many toxic substances taken in by the body. It manufactures bile. It is a screening agent against unacceptable substances entering the blood, and a filtering agent for substances which must be removed from the blood stream. The liver is the most versatile organ in the body; yet three fourths of the liver can be removed or damaged without impairment of a single function or development of any symptoms. In operations for the treatment of disease or accident most of the stomach has been removed without serious digestive or nutritional impairment. Twelve feet of small intenstine can be removed with impunity. Most of the large intestine has been removed, and the patient has suffered no considerable ill effects. Thus our bodies are constructed with a wide margin of safety.

A few concrete clinical illustrations may illuminate the concept of the margin of safety in injury and disease. There is profound blood loss in many injuries where blood vessels are cut or torn. With the blood loss there is a drop in blood pressure. Nature has provided a wide range of fluctuation of blood pressure before reaching the critical level at which the volume flow to the tissues becomes insufficient. Even with the loss of thirty to forty per cent of the blood volume there is a rapid restoration of approximately normal blood pressure. This shows that the vasomotor apparatus, which has the ability to constrict peripheral blood vessels, is organized for protection. The heart has the ability to meet extra demands. Its usual rate is seventy beats per minute; but at a moment's notice it can double its rate and output of blood, working at the same time against an increased arterial pressure.

Many stab wounds of the chest collapse all functioning lung tissue on the side of the chest involved. Such patients walk into the clinic in no great respiratory distress. In pneumonia one entire lung field may become consolidated and lose its function without dangerously interfering with the oxygen supply to the body or with the elimination of carbon dioxide.

Since brain tissue does not regenerate, many people think the factor of safety in the brain is nil. This is not true. Neurosurgeons remove tumors with surrounding segments of tissue in certain locations of the brain with no appreciable change in function or in mental characteristics. It is not uncommon for a penetrating object to be removed from the brain without leaving the patient with any neurological deficit. If a person is right-handed, his speech center is on the left side of the brain. And if he is left-handed, vice versa. If the speech center is damaged by tumor or injury, the person loses his power of speech temporarily. Then the speech center on the opposite side of the brain usually becomes activated, and the person regains the power of speech. This is a classic illustration of the body's refusal to surrender a vital function.

The blood supply to most organs is in excess, so if an artery or vein is destroyed the organ is not seriously impaired. There are already in existence collateral pathways which take immediately, by other routes, sufficient blood to the tissues of the organ. There

18

is an exception to this—that is the end arteries of the heart and brain. Such an artery is similar to a dead-end street. If an end artery in the heart muscle is blocked, the blood supply is stopped to the particular area of tissue which this end artery supplied. The disease entity which results is called a coronary thrombosis, or myocardial infarction, or by the popular term "heart attack." With proper rest and time collateral pathways are established, and this area is again supplied with blood. A similar situation involving an end artery is the stroke or cerebral vascular accident. Of course, not all strokes are related to blockage of end arteries. Often considerable damage results before collateral pathways develop because of the extreme vulnerability of brain tissue to oxygen deprivation.

The Body's Defenses

The body has a tremendous army of weapons to aid in the maintenance of its health. One of these is pain. Often one looks upon pain as an enemy and not as a friend. Pain functions as an adaptation for protection against injury. Injurious stimuli initiate reflexes which cause us to move away from the harmful agent or learn to prevent a recurrence of the injury. Another significant function of pain is that of informing us when something is going wrong and usually of telling us where the difficulty lies—a splinter in the finger, a cavity in the tooth, an inflamed appendix. The warning comes early enough to have the condition repaired before irreparable damage is done. A most fascinating function of pain is its indirect aid in the repair and replacement of damaged tissue. Rest is one of the greatest single aids to healing. Pain enforces rest in countless conditions. It may enforce rest in bed for the entire body or rest of the injured part. Pain immobilizes a broken arm, thereby facilitating growth of new bone which heals the fracture. The surgeon merely aids in the enforcement of rest of the arm by splinting it with a plaster cast.

There are many barriers against the entrance of bacteria into the body. The skin is such a barrier, and usually bacteria cannot penetrate the intact skin. Also skin secretions are often destructive of bacteria. Secretions, such as the mucus of the nose and the mouth, entrap and arrest the migration of bacteria. Tears wash the cornea and other parts of the eye free from bacteria-laden dust particles. Ciliated cells are found in the upper lung passages of humans. The cilia beat steadily in such a direction that the mucus is kept moving slowly upward. Thus bacteria and dust particles are moved out of the bronchial tubes into the pharynx.

Reflexes, such as the cough, function to expel mucus and infected or foreign particles from the respiratory system. The corneal reflex, the involuntary blinking of the eye when the cornea is touched or irritated, protects the cornea by sweeping away the intruder.

There are some interesting chemical defenses, such as the gastric juice of the stomach. Gastric juice, by virtue of its high acid content, destroys bacteria chemically, or at least retards their growth. Therefore, even though bacteria are always present in the mouth and saliva, and in the foods eaten, very few bacteria are found in the materials emptied from the stomach into the small intestine.

Infectious agents often get through the body's external barriers and produce an infection. The body has prepared for this by numerous internal defenses, such as inflammation, phagocytosis, antibody formation, and fever-producing mechanisms. When bacteria penetrate the barriers, these devices operate to localize or limit the infection. An example of reaction occurs in the formation of a boil, in which the body builds, through inflammation, a complicated wall of defense around the invading agent. If one interferes with nature by squeezing the pus out of a boil, the defensive wall is broken down, and the infection may then spread beyond the natural limiting barriers of the coagulated mass of pus and bacteria.

Phagocytosis is another device of internal defense. The phagocyte is a cell that ingests microorganisms or other cells and substances. In most cases the ingested material is digested within the phagocyte. Phagocytes are either fixed to one particular location or free to move about. A prominent place for phagocytosis is the lymph system of the body.

Lymph vessels and nodes are barriers against generalized spread. If the bacteria gain entrance into the lymphatic vessels, they are filtered out into the lymph nodes in large numbers and ingested by the phagocytic cells found in the meshes of the nodes. Lymph nodes and vessels are abundant in areas where bacteria are most likely to gain entrance—about the pharynx and the respiratory and gastrointestinal passages. Often so much bacteria is filtered out in the lymph nodes along a vessel draining an infected area that the node becomes swollen. Every person has experienced painful swellings of the neck during a sore throat, or in the axilla after cutting a finger, or in the groin after sticking a nail in the bare foot. The "kernels" are swollen lymph nodes which have been on active duty in our army of defense against infectious agents.

When the agencies for the limitation of the spread of the bacteria fail to localize the infection, the combat between invader and defenses continues in all parts of the body where the organisms spread. One of the major defense mechanisms is acquired immunity. The antibodies produced by the body do one of several things: destroy bacteria by dissolving them; clump the bacteria, which prevents their spread; neutralize the poisons produced by the bacteria; or precipitate the toxins formed.

Adjustive Techniques of the Mind

We have seen that the body reacts in a highly coordinated fashion when confronted with disease or injury. A study of dynamic behavior has shown that the mind does the same. Its reactions to the stresses and strains of everyday living are by no means random. We are filled with primitive urges, instincts, and impulses that demand gratification and which often must be expressed. Through mental mechanisms, such as sublimation, we find outlets in ways that use this energy for actions and activities that are acceptable to society and often very useful. Thus the term "homeostasis" can be used to refer to mental functioning as well as physiological processes.

21

The same vital principle within the individual that has the capacity for maintaining effective, coordinated, physiological functioning under constantly changing conditions of life can be applied also to the balanced functioning of the mind and the dynamic equilibrium of the individual with his social environment. The strength of the strivings for happiness and health which are part of the natural equipment of man is remarkably impressive.

The psychological devices which man has evolved help him to meet such emotional needs as those for affection, personal security, self-esteem, and for defense against perturbing anxiety. By acting without conscious awareness on one's part these mental devices effect an adjustment to inner situations and experiences that otherwise could be intolerably distressing. The personality, with its profound need for security and a feeling of self-esteem, evokes mechanisms of a protective nature as instinctively as self-preservation incites the avoidance of approaching physical danger. Thus, the mind, through autonomic and unconscious psychological processes, seeks to maintain a psychological stability not unlike the physiological equilibrium which the body seeks to maintain. Various techniques are used by the mind as attempts to enhance and defend itself, to establish acceptable compromises between conflicting impulses, and to allay inner tensions. Through these internal mechanisms of control, which are unconscious and automatic, the mind develops defenses designed to manage anxiety, aggressive impulses, hostilities, resentments, and frustrations.

The adjustive techniques used by the mind are so standardized and systematized that they are called mental or defense mechanisms. A defense mechanism is a way of reacting, a way of handling a situation involving conflicting impulses. A few of these mechanisms which are relatively healthy are compensation, rationalization, idealization, reaction formation, and displacement. There are a multitude of others which are equally important but cannot be discussed because of limitations of space.

Compensation is an unconscious mechanism by which the person tries to make up for fancied or real weakness. One usually

22

tries to compensate for handicaps or limitations. Milton, in his blindness, wrote magnificent literature. Beethoven composed his great symphonies while growing more and more deaf.

The term "rationalization" was introduced into psychiatric literature by the great psychiatrist Ernest Jones. It is one of the most common devices designed to maintain self-respect and prevent feelings of guilt. It is a self-adjusting mechanism by which one first acts in response to unrecognized motives and after the action offers various supposed "reasons" for the action. Through rationalization one explains very convincingly and apparently logically to make a thing appear reasonable, when otherwise its irrationality would be evident. Rationalization is nonconscious and thus has no relation to lying.

Rationalization can lead to self-deception, and its conclusions are not trustworthy guides for further conduct. This is also the "sour grapes" mechanism. In this defensive maneuver the individual disparages some particular goal which, inwardly at least, he would greatly like to attain, but which because of some obstacle, often personal inadequacy, he cannot reach.

Idealization is an unconscious overestimation of an admired attribute of another. When one feels that his sweetheart is the loveliest woman in the whole world, he is using this mechanism.

Reaction formation is a kind of reversal. If an unconscious impulse to express itself is so strong in one direction, the only way the conscious mind can control it is to do the opposite. Some of our compulsive behavior of cleanliness and orderliness represents the very opposite from the way we would like to behave. Perfectionistic and uncompromising character traits are often reaction formations against forbidden tendencies, desires, or impulses. Feelings of rejection and hostility may be disguised by scrupulous politeness or effusive expressions of gratitude. The overtly aggressive person who constantly demands his rights and is ready to fight at any provocation may be defending himself against a deeply seated sense of insecurity.

Displacement is an anxiety-reducing device by which the emotional value attached to one idea or person is transferred to another idea or person. The wife who shouts angrily at her child because her husband refused to take her to the party is displacing the anger meant for her husband upon her child.

The mind protects itself against anxiety with the use of defense mechanisms. These mechanisms solve the conflict between the instinctual impulses and the rational, civilized mind. Our personality uses them without our conscious knowledge, to help us keep a sense of balance and some degree of peace of mind. Thus psychological homeostasis is maintained as automatically and naturally as physiological homeostasis.

From where does the physiological and psychological homeostasis come? Since the earliest days of medical practice physicians usually recognized that there was a power greater than themselves at work in the recovery of their patients. Whether this power is called God or nature or homeostasis is not important, for it is the recognition and acknowledgment of such a power that leads to the attitude of reverence in our work and relationships with human life. Since we need a fixed point of reference, a final cause and final answer by which to orient our human efforts, we can find it in this greater wisdom which controls the complex reactions of our human bodies.

His daily work reaffirms afresh for the physician the mystery of life, whose laws he has partly learned in his efforts to remove the obstacles to healing, to renewal, to resurrection.

In discussing homeostasis from a psychological point of view I am not suggesting a mechanistic concept of man like that of a machine in neutral gear, therefore in balance. I am in agreement with Viktor Frankl's concept of man as possessing innate strivings for ontologically significant goals, strivings for attainment of a meaning in life. Frankl has postulated in man an inborn drive which he calls the "will to meaning." Thus, one strives to find purpose in one's own existence, to find a sense of mission that is uniquely one's own and that gives direction to one's life. The individual integrates his life around meaningful goals. Clinical studies of man have shown that he is a purposive, striving organism with possibly a will to meaning as a part of his original makeup. The organism must continually strive for something, even though it be simply an escape from monotony.

2

Spiritual Concerns and Mental Health

A chaplain's experience at the close of World War II focuses on a problem of modern man which is of major concern to workers in both psychiatry and religion.

The naval hospital ship on which the chaplain was serving was transporting a load of liberated Allied prisoners of war—most of them sick—from Japan to San Francisco. The ship, sailing at a rapid speed, began to vibrate, for the seas were heavy.

A call for the chaplain came over the public-address system. He was wanted by a sick former prisoner who had been a civilian engineer on Wake Island, and who had been captured there by the Japanese. He had pulmonary tuberculosis with bilateral cavitation and was terminal.

He told the chaplain, "I feel I am dying. The vibrating ship bothers me no end. I don't want to die at sea. Would it be possible for the ship to stop at Guam and put me off there so I could die near Wake Island, where I lived and worked?" The chaplain speculated that what the patient feared was being buried at sea if he died. The sick man went on to say, "I am frightened and alone. I have no philosophy of life adequate for living or dying. I always went to church and was reared in a religious home. But all I was given in church was a series of negatives—don't do this, don't do that—about smoking, dancing, card playing, and other forms of social activity.

"In prison camp, where I remained for almost four years, I had no philosophy for living, and now I have no philosophy for dying. Although it is late, almost midnight in my life, would you help me find a philosophy for dying, a meaning in death, a purpose behind my suffering?"

The chaplain's first reaction was to blame the church for

letting this man down, for stressing nonessentials, for having failed him.

On second thought, and on further exploration, he realized that this individual was more responsible for his present state than was the church from which he came.

He had never really been interested in a basic philosophy of life or a basic philosophy concerning death and its meaning. If such a concern crept into his mind, he had pushed it away because of fear, anxiety, lack of interest, or a preoccupation with other matters.

Actually, the chaplain should not have blamed either the church or the individual. The sick man was a child of his age, and he was reflecting the emptiness of his particular culture. Now he was presenting the tragic picture that one sees not infrequently, the picture of a person who only begins to live when he begins to die.

Modern Man in Search

What this sick engineer had been doing was "waiting for Godot." The play *Waiting for Godot*, written by Samuel Beckett, an Irish disciple of James Joyce, is one in which "nothingness" is reflected in every line from beginning to end. It played to packed houses in the capitals of Europe for more than sixteen months. It was presented in New York and played to capacity audiences there and in many of the little theaters throughout the United States.

One can conclude that these audiences recognized something of their own experiences in what they saw on the stage—some echo, however veiled, of their own emptiness and, in Heidegger's phrase, their own "waiting for God."

The chaplain's conversation and experience with his dying patient awakened in him an interest to explore the meaning of life and death and the dimensions of our existence. Similar experiences, involving themselves or others, were reported by many men and women directly or indirectly involved in World War II. Many of these individuals, seasoned in war and disappointed in peace, have found themselves at work in many disciplines, seeking answers to the problems of individual and group life.

In art, literature, and in many other forms of communication modern man is beginning to realize that he has been "waiting for Godot." He has discovered his emptiness.

Erich Fromm has repeatedly stressed the fact that after man broke his primary bonds to nature and developed his supreme individuality, he found himself alone, isolated, and anxious. The contemplation of the future, of his own destiny, and of his finiteness, contributed toward making him more anxious.

Modern man—alone and in exile—has taken a look at the old orthodoxy, which once served to allay this anxiety, and has found it unpalatable. The church to him is somewhat like a hypochondriac widow who draws the blinds and lives with the mementos of her dead husband.

At other times he has found the church so occupied with the setting or matrix that the precious stone or jewel in its possession is covered up or unnoticed. He has found many sermons dealing with warmed-over material, not properly digested by the minister, and concerned with symbols and language no longer meaningful to modern man. He then turns from orthodoxy to liberalism and finds only a partial answer there. The humanistic tradition gives him a framework for altruism and service but no real orientation as to his nature and destiny and for understanding his predicament.

What does modern man do? He tries to forget it all in order to avoid facing the fundamental issues. He gathers around himself all kinds of noise makers—TV, hi-fi, FM, stereo—crowding every hour with activity. He even begins to feel safe, at least for awhile.

Then one night, long before day, he awakens, and in the awful stillness of the night he feels his own heartbeat, his own respirations, and with this acute self-consciousness he begins to ponder.

He murmurs to himself, "What is man; who am I; where am I going; what is my destiny; someday I'll not exist; where will I go?" He becomes filled with anxiety. He examines his life and finds that none of his goals really have been satisfactorily attained. A kind of metaphysical unrest sweeps over him, a kind of guilt he cannot shake off.

So, in his solitude, the discovery of his aloneness takes place—his exile, his anxiety, his guilt. As Søren Kierkegaard has said, "There comes a midnight hour when all men must unmask."

Theologians and psychiatrists are both concerned with man's anxiety and guilt.[1] Anxiety seems to be a part of man's basic endowment, an ontological characteristic of man, rooted in his very existence. It has been stressed that anxiety is not something we "have" but something we "are."

Man experiences his anxiety whenever he contemplates his finiteness, the threat of nonbeing, the threat of the loss of existence itself. The terms "metaphysical," "ontological," or "existential" all identify this type of anxiety which is the condition of the individual when he is confronted with the predicament of his existence, the issue of fulfilling his potentialities.

When the person denies these potentialities, and fails to fulfill them or live up to his highest expectations, his condition is guilt, for guilt is also an ontological characteristic of human existence.[2]

---

[1] An illuminating discussion of anxiety by both theologians and psychiatrists is found in *Constructive Aspects of Anxiety*, ed. Seward Hiltner and Karl Menninger (Nashville: Abingdon Press, 1963).

[2] Ontological guilt and anxiety are not to be confused with neurotic guilt and anxiety. Possibly the proper grouping of guilt would encompass three areas: (1) real or normal guilt; (2) neurotic guilt; and (3) existential guilt. Normal guilt follows in the wake of wrongdoing, seen and accepted as such by the doer. He seeks expiation and makes restitution. It is a conscious phenomenon involving deeds he has done. Neurotic guilt has its roots deep in the unconscious mind, and the individual cannot rid himself of this by usual methods of atonement. In neurotic guilt, the intent, even unconscious, is equated with the deed, and the person reacts to the unconscious intent as if it were an already accomplished misdeed. Ontological guilt refers to a guilt innate in man and part of the very structure of being human. No one completely reaches the goals he has set or should have set for himself. Also, who can say that his interpersonal relationships have been and are what they should be? Often they are disrupted with failures in communication or tendencies to use others for one's own sake. Thus ontological guilt is nourished by one's failure to live up to his potentialities and his failures in interpersonal relationships.

Anxiety can be grouped into categories similar to guilt: normal, neurotic, and ontological. The categories, however, are not as precise as when referring to guilt. Whenever possibility is visualized by an individual, normal anxiety is potentially present in the experience. Every person has the opportunity and need

Since our society is both secular and religious, modern man, anxious and guilt-ridden, often turns to the professional person in the psychological sciences to help him solve his problem of meaning and anxiety. Psychiatry is forced to deal with concerns and values essentially the same as those of the church, and trouble begins when the domains overlap.

Some people's concept of religion is that of following the Golden Rule, and their concept of psychiatry is that of a branch of medicine which occupies itself with the insane in specially designated hospitals.

When religion and psychiatry are defined in these terms, one does not have to worry about the influence of either one on modern man in search of meaning.

Psychiatry today, however, is not confined to mental hospitals; it has reached out to concern itself with every aspect of human behavior and both internal and external relationships. It goes into the conflicts and anxieties of everyday life and into the world of love and hatred which unites or separates human beings.

Its most significant implement of treatment is psychotherapy —a purely psychological method of treatment in which the physician himself, to a great extent, becomes an instrument of therapy and without those chemical and physical means one commonly associates with medicine.

Religion today is not, to a great number of people, a vague understanding of the command to be a nice person and follow the Golden Rule; rather, it represents a set of truths about the

---

to move ahead in his development. These possibilities are roads which one does not know, for he has not yet traveled them. Thus, anxiety is involved, that is, normal anxiety. In each case the anxiety is proportionate to an objective threat, does not involve repression or intrapsychic conflict, and can be met with the person's own powers without retrenchment into neurotic defense mechanisms. Neurotic anxiety is usually defined as a reaction to threat which is disproportionate to the objective danger and involves repression and other forms of intrapsychic conflict. Neurotic anxiety is managed by means of various forms of retrenchment of activity and awareness, such as inhibitions, the development of symptoms and the varied neurotic defense mechanisms. Ontological anxiety is a characteristic rooted in man's very existence, the experience of the threat of imminent nonbeing. The individual's becoming aware that the rug of his existence could be pulled out from under him is the root of ontological anxiety.

nature and destiny of man, about human bondage, and transcendental values.

When man's origin and destiny are discussed, one finds that he cannot really talk about man without bringing God into it: namely, in specific terms of creation and salvation. Thus many of the concerns of present-day psychiatry and religion are mutual, and it is challenging and necessary to discuss religion as it relates to mental health.

No person can talk about the anxiety and the love and the hatred of human beings without giving some thought to the nature of man. One cannot have a definite set of beliefs about the origin and destiny of man without being haunted by the mystery of human anxiety and guilt.

Finding Some Answers for Modern Man

The cooperative efforts of psychiatry and religion may well result in helping modern man find answers to some of his crucial questions on his predicament.

The church has often emphasized love as one of the chief virtues. It is significant that psychiatry is emphasizing that the answer to man's isolation and aloneness is in relatedness to and solidarity with his fellow man. Once Freud was asked what he would consider the ultimate in being normal, and he replied: "*Arbeiten und lieben*"—to work and to love.

Unremitting creative effort and love of one's neighbor are the human values affirmed. Both religion and psychiatry agree that life can be ordered to good ends which enrich and fulfill personal and communal life. They share a common belief that love and truth generate an atmosphere in which human character matures and is transformed.

A major philosophical movement aiding greatly in the cooperative efforts of many groups, such as psychiatry, psychology, philosophy, and the social sciences, is existentialism.[3]

[3] Existentialism does not lend itself to an easy definition. It is a universal element in all human thinking in the attempt of man to describe his existence and its conflicts, to discover the origin of these conflicts, and the anticipation of overcoming them.

This philosophical movement has furnished a platform upon which these different groups with varying professional and personal commitments and beliefs can meet, without apology or compromise, to discuss such matters as anxiety, death, the overcoming of man's separateness, the conflict between the counterfeit and the genuine self, the faceless man of the masses, and the "waiting for Godot."

The groups involved in existentialism are seeking deeper insights into the inner depth of the psychic life of man which cannot be measured by the quantitative methods of the physical sciences. Grouped together among the existentialists are Jews, Roman Catholics, and Protestants, as well as atheists. The existential philosophers recast the meaning of religion and religious faith in relation to the individual. They are more concerned with the predicament of man than with his nature.

In recent years there has been an artificial separation of psychological and philosophical matters. The great ethical thinkers of the past were both philosophers and psychologists. These men believed that the understanding of man's nature and the understanding of values and norms for his life were interdependent.

The many disciplines attracted to existentialism find that in the flexible framework of existentialism human values and ethics are vital concerns, both theoretically and therapeutically, not just of clergymen but of all who seek to understand and modify hu-

---

Existentialism is not a philosophy but a name given to several widely different revolts against traditional philosophy. It is basically concerned with ontology, that is, the science of being. Thus, existentialism is an attitude which accepts man as always becoming. It deals more with the psychological predicament of contemporary Western man than with his nature. A political scientist has said that existentialism implies that human effort is at one and the same time an essay in creativity and a meditation on failure.

This modern emotional and spiritual temper called existentialism expresses itself in almost all aspects of our culture. It is found in psychology, art, philosophy, and literature. The themes are often familiar Christian ones: the decision to join the innocent sufferers rather than the sinful conquerors; the torments of the guilty conscience; the pained cry for redemption; tragic characters in life's drama, who can at least glimpse heroic nobility. Theologians have commented that many existentialists are able to cry out, "My God, my God, why hast thou forsaken me?" but are unable to say, "Father, into thy hands I commend my spirit."

31

man behavior. Thus, this false separation or dichotomy, hopefully, may be eliminated.

The study of religious psychopathology by both theologians and psychological scientists will give us a new understanding and appreciation of religious growth and development. Medicine, through the study of disease processes and pathological states, has learned a great deal about normal physiology.

The eminent mental-hospital chaplain Anton Boisen often encouraged chaplains, psychiatrists, and psychologists to study abnormal religious behavior, not in order to depreciate or become overly familiar with the sacred, but to discover a new and deeper understanding of normal religious growth and development.

3

The Substance of Mental Health

When man was new upon the earth he was frightened by the dangers of the elements. He did not know the meaning of lightning, thunder, and rain. Many of the harsh elements of nature seemed to be arrayed against him and often caused him bodily discomfort. He first found protection in the caves of the earth, and then he built shelters to protect himself against these elements.

Within man himself have raged storms—strong forces which have frightened him and often made his mind sick. Through the centuries he has been afraid to face the mystery of his inner self. He has not found wisdom to build shelters against the fierce elements which raged within as he had built shelters to protect himself from external elements.

He has continued to conquer the physical world, and now today in the nuclear age his hands have wrought miracles too great to comprehend. Yet, emotionally, he has remained in the Stone Age.

Emotional development has been so charted that we know the path the child must take to emotional health and maturity. We know that mature men can live and work together in love and peace. We know that man finds his fulfillment only in relatedness to and solidarity with his fellow men. In spite of this knowledge there is little peace in the world and little peace in the hearts of men.

There have been many definitions of mental health, and they all seem inadequate. Actually the term cannot be defined briefly with any degree of satisfaction.

A gasoline station operator discovered that by keeping his emotional accounts in balance, he maintained an effective level of mental health. A customer rolled into the gas station after having a flat tire and asked the service station operator, whom he had never seen before, if the old spare was still usable. The man put a patch on the tube and in response to the question, "How much?" said, "It's on the house." The customer commented, "It's very kind of you, but why are you doing this for a stranger?" "Well," he replied, "yesterday I woke up as mean as a beaver with a toothache. I bit everybody who came in sight. This morning I feel fine. So today I am making up for yesterday. Favors for the customers—kind words for the help. That is how I pay off for the bad days."

Few of us balance our emotional accounts as promptly and scrupulously. We permit our debits to grow to staggering proportions and then are overwhelmed by them. But when one day's crabbiness is paid off by the next day's benevolence, the slate is wiped clean. There is no lingering residue of remorse to haunt us.

The National Association for Mental Health has been very helpful in identifying and emphasizing to the public many of the characteristics which seem to make for good mental health. These characteristics are usually grouped into three broad categories. Mentally healthy persons (1) feel comfortable about themselves; (2) feel right about other people; and (3) are able to meet the demands of life. In this discussion the material will be grouped under these three headings for clarity in presentation.

They Feel Comfortable About Themselves

They feel comfortable about their own bodies. Such people are unashamed of the body and its physiological functions. The human body is miraculous in a thousand different ways. The various functions of the organs and the parts of the body and their ability to repair themselves are rare and wonderful gifts of God. One should not fear to turn the spotlight on his physical self. A high-school principal received a letter from a mother whose child was just beginning the study of physiology: "I don't want my Mary to learn no more about her insides." Thus, intimate self-examination even in the physical realm is frightening to many people.

In one's appreciation of his physical body he should develop the ability to live within the limits imposed by bodily equipment. Many persons consciously or unconsciously seek to destroy or abuse the body. It is a machine that does require care. It does not last well when the candle is burned at both ends. The scriptural reminder is a searching one: "Know ye not that your body is the temple of the Holy Ghost?"

They are not bowled over by their emotions. They may experience fear, anger, love, jealousy, guilt, or worry but know the meaning of these in relationship to their thoughts and actions. They learn to know the evidence of mental disturbances and how best to deal with depressions, temper tantrums, and other forms of ill health. They recognize neurotic evasions as such and take advantage of opportunities to sublimate this energy into creative activity.

They have a careful blending of independence and dependence—aggression and passivity. Our culture expects the man to be aggressive and the woman to be dependent and passive. Actually there is a blending of both in the normal person with the proper one dominant according to sex. The improper blending of these two characteristics has caused confusion in role definition and sexual identification.

In our country, men are more affected by bottled-up dependence, and women by bottled-up aggression. Without suggesting a cause-and-effect connection it is interesting to note that ulcers, a disease considered to be accelerated by unsatisfied yearnings to be loved and protected, have been occurring about five times as frequently in men as in women. On the other hand, gall-bladder trouble, involving the production of bile, which since the time of Hippocrates has been a synonym for anger and venom, has been occurring with greater frequency in women than in men. Whether milk as the major ingredient of the ulcer diet helps more in its capacity as an antacid or as a symbol of maternal affection is one of the many unanswered questions of the whole problem.

A chief concern of the male is his masculinity and that of the female her feminine desirability. A woman is much more interested in what her man tells her than in what her mirror tells her. Although the roles may be somewhat confused today on the American scene, the basic nature of human beings is not changing. The woman still believes that the finest words to come from her man are, "I love you." The words a man likes to hear from his woman are, "I am so proud of you." As Anatole France said: "A woman who insists on equality renounces her superiority."

They feel able to deal with most situations which come their way. They can take life's frustrations and disappointments in their stride. Shakespeare speaks to our age as to his when he says:

> Sweet are the uses of adversity,
> Which like the toad, ugly and venomous,
> Wears yet a precious jewel in its head.

Violins are not made from just any kind of wood. The violin makers of old cut their wood from the timberline, where the trees had constant exposure to the fierce elements of nature. The refining and disciplining influences of life are well illustrated in the poem written by an unknown Confederate soldier:

> I asked God for strength, that I might achieve,
> I was made weak, that I might learn humbly to obey . . . .
> I asked for health, that I might do greater things,
> I was given infirmity, that I might do better things . . . .
> I asked for riches, that I might be happy,
> I was given poverty that I might be wise . . . .
> I asked for power, that I might have the praise of men,
> I was given weakness, that I might feel the need of God . . . .
> I asked for all things, that I might enjoy life,
> I was given life, that I might enjoy all things . . . .
> I got nothing that I asked for—but everything I had hoped for,
> Almost despite myself, my unspoken prayers were answered.
> I am among all men, most richly blessed.[1]

[1] As printed in John Ellis Large, *Think on These Things* (New York: Harper & Bros., 1954).

A similar and even more meaningful illustration of the capacity of man to rise above adversity is the situation of Hans Zinsser. He was a distinguished bacteriologist, widely known and renowned for his scientific accomplishments and his excellent writings. While at the very peak of his medical career he was found to have leukemia and knew that in a matter of months he would die. After discovering this fact he went on living positively and wrote a beautiful book of sonnets for his wife entitled *Spring, Summer and Autumn.*

A couplet written in 1591 by John Florio also illustrates the blending of patience in suffering and strength in action:

> When you are anvil hold you still;
> When you are hammer strike your fill.

They have a tolerant, easygoing attitude toward themselves. The mentally healthy person can laugh at himself. He neither overestimates nor underestimates his abilities. He can accept his own shortcomings and assume responsibility for his mistakes. A saying by Wang Yang-Mind, a fifteenth-century Chinese philosopher and statesman, has given hope and cheer to many in a personal crisis: "The sages do not consider that making no mistakes is a blessing. They believe, rather, that the great virtue of man lies in his ability to correct his mistakes and continually to make a new man of himself."

The healthy person has self-respect and self-esteem. Many persons are too critical of themselves and suffer from self-depreciation. The Scriptures not only allow but encourage us to love ourselves, implying that if one can love himself he is then able to love his neighbor. Personal security and inner security come with self-esteem and self-respect.

They have the ability to experience both pleasure and pain—not one or none but both. Feeling tone is an important factor in mental health, and one must be able to experience both pleasure and pain. If one has known the anguish of pain, he can then know joy in greater fullness.

They possess a grown-up conscience. A mature, well-developed conscience is one of man's greatest assets. Civilization could not endure without it. An overdeveloped conscience pushes the individual toward neurotic guilt and all kinds of obsessive, compulsive behavior. The underdeveloped conscience permits him to be psychopathic and extractive in his behavior. The well-developed conscience, not too strict or too easy, permits the individual to live at peace with himself and his fellow man. If he does wrong, he is aware of it, feels guilty, and is constrained to correct his wrong. When he has made restitution, he is comfortable with himself again.

They Feel Right and Comfortable About Other People

They are able to give love and receive love. In 1768 the *Encyclopaedia Britannica* had four sentences on the atom and five pages on love. In a recent edition of the *Britannica* there are nine pages on the atom and nothing on love.

Søren Kierkegaard, in *Fear and Trembling*, tells a legendary story of a girl whose groom, each time she marries, is killed on the wedding night by a demon who is in love with the bride. This is the background story on which he writes philosophically about the bride and each groom. He states that love came toward this girl, and she was able to receive it, although the experience ended each time in tragedy and misfortune. He goes on to say that although her despair was great, it was not nearly so great as the one to whom love came and who was unable to receive it. The latter situation, Kierkegaard says, is one of unfathomable sorrow. He further states that the mystery is that it is better to give than to receive, but a greater mystery is that it is far more difficult to receive than to give.

The importance of love is nowhere more pungently expressed than in the words of Paul: "If I speak with the tongues of men and of angels, but have not love, I am a noisy gong, or a clanging cymbal. And if I have prophetic powers, and understand all mysteries and all knowledge, and if I have all faith, so as to remove mountains, but have not love, I am nothing" (I Cor. 13: 1-2, RSV).

The church has a tendency to fragment love so that there is one type of love which a human feels for another, a different type of love which man feels for God, and another type which God feels for man. *Eros* is the first, *agape* the second, and *philanthropia* the third. These terms were introduced into the religious vocabulary at a comparatively late date. Originally the word "love" was used by the church fathers almost in the erotic sense. In an article in the *Supplement to La Vie Spirituelle* (1950), there is a very interesting contribution entitled "Eros et Agape," by H. C. Graef. The author shows that between the second and fifth centuries the word eros was considered the proper one to designate the supernatural love. It seems that the religious leaders, in presenting to their flocks and to their pagan world a God whom they loved as the supreme object of their desires, were unable to avoid indefinitely the word which imposed itself upon them. They did what the church has always done—they took a depreciated concept and infused it with a new significance. In this article we read that Ignatius of Antioch, one of the earliest Christian martyrs, wrote, "My love [eros] is crucified, and I have in me no longer the fire of love for material things." Origen, one of the early church fathers, wrote that the terms agape and eros are interchangeable. John Chrysostom speaks of "the Eros of the Lord the Father toward men." Chrysostom also speaks of a "spiritual Eros," of his eros for Paul, for truth, and also for the kingdom of heaven. Graef concludes that "from the beginning of the 5th Century on, Eros seems to have become a generally accepted synonym for Agape."

Psychiatry has rediscovered the primary position of love in man's world. Psychiatry and the church can find common cause in reemphasizing the crucial importance of love in individual and group life.

They have personal relationships that are satisfying and lasting. They expect to like and trust others, and take it for granted that others will like and trust them. They are not frightened by the closeness of another human being. They respect the many differences they find in people. Thomas à Kempis has written,

"How seldom we weigh our neighbor in the same balance with ourselves."

They do not push other people around, nor do they allow themselves to be pushed around. A prominent white southern minister was once invited to fill the pulpit at a Negro church and accepted with grace. His stirring sermon had to do with the glories of the hereafter, and he took occasion to repeat several times this extraordinary point: "Up yonder the white folks will walk down streets paved with pure gold, and even the colored folks will walk down streets paved with asphalt!" The congregation, out of politeness to a visitor, seemed inclined to let this projection of the South upon heaven pass unnoticed, but the deacon who offered the closing prayer was moved to observe: ". . . and deeply grateful as we are for your bringing your servant to interpret the Scriptures for us, you know, Lord, like we know, that when and if colored folks get to heaven they are going to walk where they damn please!"

They can feel they are part of a group and never isolated from the mainstream of humanity. John Donne has pointed out for us the bonds which tie together all human beings:

No man is an Island, intire of it selfe; every man is a peece of the Continent, a part of the maine; if a Clod bee washed away by the Sea, Europe is the lesse, as well as if a Promontorie were, as well as if a Mannor of thy friends or of thine owne were; any mans death diminishes me, because I am involved in Mankinde; And therefore never send to know for whom the bell tolls; It tolls for thee.

They feel a sense of responsibility to their neighbors and fellow men. Am I my brother's keeper? The answer has always been and still is "yes."

A story worth pondering is that of the scene of the Last Judgment described in the New Testament, when the sheep are separated from the goats. The separation is made on the basis of what one has done for others and not on the basis of doctrine, church, or theology.

They do not have too great a resentment of authority. In the process of socialization each individual has had profoundly meaningful experiences with authority figures. If his experiences have been with harsh authority figures, he usually has a tendency to rebel openly or to smother his need to rebel with excessive submission. If his experiences have been mostly with benevolent authority figures, he will be more comfortable with those in society who represent authority. Too great a resentment of authority can often be self-defeating and even self-destructive.

They Are Able to Meet the Demands of Life

They face reality as honestly and cheerfully as possible. They have the ability to be guided by reality rather than by fears and fantasies. A dramatic illustration of not facing reality is seen in Tennessee Williams' *The Rose Tattoo.* A truck driver's wife has an intense need for her husband to be perfect. She idolizes him, although he is quite human and has another woman whom he meets on his trips. The truck driver is killed in an accident. His ashes are given to his wife in an urn, which she places in the center of her living room on the mantel. She prays to her dead husband regularly. The story reaches its climax when her husband's past infidelity is made known to her. She crashes the urn to bits, becomes completely disorganized, and plunges into a psychotic episode.

They have the ability to meet competition. They demonstrate a reasonable aggressiveness. The family teaches cooperation and competition. One thinks of the family mostly as a cooperative unit, but there is much competition—for the use of radio, TV, affection, the family car, and other items and experiences.

Some people compete on every turn and in situations that will profit them nothing. Every driver has had the experience of trying to pass a car and having the driver of the other car immediately and almost spontaneously increase the speed of his car and prevent the other car from passing him.

They shape their environment whenever possible; they adjust to it whenever necessary. No words summarize this concept better than the prayer written by Reinhold Niebuhr:

41

God grant me the serenity to accept those things I cannot change, the courage to change the things I can and the wisdom to know the difference.

The healthy person plans ahead but does not fear the future. He welcomes new experiences and new ideas. He is not like the elderly gentleman who, when asked whether he had seen many new things in his time, replied: "Yes and I have been against every one of them." He makes use of his natural capacities, searches out his own talents, develops them, and uses them. He sets realistic goals for himself. He extends his best efforts and derives satisfaction from accomplishment. Eight hundred years ago, S'hota Rustaveli, a Georgian poet of the Caucasus, wrote in his epic, *The Man in the Panther's Skin*, these words:

> What you keep is lost—
> What you give is forever yours.

These words have given men a pattern for friendship, and shortly after Rustaveli wrote them they belonged to a whole people.

They accept their responsibilities. They are able to think for themselves and make their own decisions. They obey the rules of the game of life with grace and cheerfulness.

They do something about their problems as they arise. The illustration about the service station operator is one approach to the understanding of this statement.

They live without being a nuisance. Many writers in the field of mental health stress the importance of this point. George Bernard Shaw, in the Preface to *Man and Superman*, writes: "This is the true joy in life, the being used for a purpose recognized by yourself as a mighty one; the being thoroughly worn out before you are thrown on the scrap heap; the being a force of Nature instead of a feverish selfish little clod of ailments and grievances complaining that the world will not devote itself to making you happy."

They appreciate the use of long-term values. So often a person desires immediate gratification of every wish or impulse. He is unable to sacrifice or discipline himself today in order to realize a significant and far-reaching goal tomorrow.

They utilize healthy defense mechanisms. In order to maintain our mental equilibrium, to properly channel various types of energies, and to reach compromises between our conscience and our instinctual impulses, we bring into use many mental mechanisms which enable us to sail smoothly through seas which are at times stormy. Some of these mental mechanisms are sublimation, compensation, introjection, displacement, identification, repression, suppression, projection, denial, and reaction formation. These are discussed in greater detail in the chapter entitled "The Body's Miraculous Wisdom."

They maintain good sexual adjustment, each accepting his own gender. The man should be able to function adequately as a man in the heterosexual role, and the woman should be able to function adequately in her feminine role as wife and mother. Today's culture is filled with all types of sexual cripples, evidencing a variety of blurred sexual identifications. These manifest themselves in various forms of sexual deviation. Solutions are sometimes sought in alcoholism and criminal behavior.

They have good work adjustments. Many people do not like their work. The reasons for this are many. Some never find work suited to their particular talents. Some are unable to obtain the necessary education and preparation for the type of work they want. Others, with adequate preparation in their own choice of job, still do not enjoy working. Some have unrealistic fantasies of the rewards a job should bring. Young men with education and ability often find it discouraging to start at the bottom without the benefits of prestige or a large salary. Many girls, in undertaking marriage, have difficulty in beginning on a small scale and a small budget.

Some employees are made anxious by the responsibilities of a job. They feel rejection, criticism, and ridicule, or they fail to obtain the approval and appreciation that they need from employer and fellow worker. Consequently, they develop tension. This tension may manifest itself in complaints, irritability, and poor cooperation. It may go further and disturb body functioning to produce symptoms such as headaches, fatigue, loss of appetite, nausea, diarrhea.

Many children are not taught cooperative living through work assignments at home. They miss the important concept that work must be done by everyone if the individual and the nation are to prosper. Instead of feeling a strong need to produce, and learning early to enjoy cooperative effort and service, they grow up with the need to be served and taken care of by "others." These "others" turn out to be employer, industry, husband, wife, community or government institutions.

Conclusion

Mental health is far more than merely the absence of mental illness. On some level of his awareness every person wants mental health, and he speaks of it when he mentions happiness, or peace of mind, or satisfaction. There is no clearly marked line that neatly divides the mentally healthy from the unhealthy. Possibly nobody has all the traits of good mental health all the time. The best way of describing mental health is to describe mentally healthy people: those who feel comfortable about themselves, who feel right about other people, and who are able to meet the demands of life are persons from whom much can be learned about mental health.

The mentally healthy person continues to grow, develop, and mature. He is in the process of being born as long as he is alive, for he considers the gift of life the most precious chance he has and seeks continuously to use this gift effectively. He makes productive use of his specifically human powers and is capable of relating himself lovingly to his fellow men.

He accepts the requirements and the opportunities of each successive stage of life from infancy through the now available years of old age. He finds the fulfillment these years offer without paying too high a cost personally or socially, as he participates in maintaining social order and carrying on our culture.

II
PIONEERS

4

Carl Gustav Jung: Religious and Psychological Concerns

At a time when man is no longer threatened by natural catastrophes or the danger of worldwide epidemics, but by man himself, the voice of Carl Gustav Jung rings clear in offering a prescription for hope. His emphasis is on the individual and his need to be regenerated in spirit. If the individual does not find redemption, neither can society.[1] He has pleaded for the recognition of the existence of good and evil in every individual and a true understanding of the inner self. The goal of the individual should be integrated wholeness and not perfection.

Although a biographical sketch is beyond the scope of this chapter, a few facts about Jung's life are essential to an understanding of his work. He was born on July 26, 1875, in the town of Kesswil, near Basel, Switzerland. His father was a Protestant clergyman. There were both physicians and biblical scholars among his ancestors. In 1900 he received his medical degree from the University of Basel. After that he took postgraduate training in psychiatry at the famous Burghölzli Hospital in Zurich and remained a prominent member of its staff for several years. His distinguished work at the Burghölzli Hospital led to a personal meeting and active collaboration with Freud. In

---

[1] This is in contrast with the view of Erich Fromm as expressed in such writings as *Escape from Freedom*, *Man for Himself*, and *The Sane Society*. For Fromm, society is the patient. Man is simply the victim of bad and evil society and is suffering and isolated. Thus man's freedom and wholeness depend not upon mastering his own passions and humbling his own pride but upon the reform of society. Fromm has emphasized repeatedly his conviction that our civilization relentlessly and systematically crushes and corrupts man's deepest needs and noblest powers. It should be mentioned that while Jung's emphasis is upon the individual he does not hold society in high regard. At many points his criticism goes beyond Fromm's, for Fromm puts more hope in the creative possibilities of a transformed society than does Jung.

1913 a break occurred between the two and from that time on Jung worked independently of Freud but in close association with many colleagues and followers. Jung died at his home in Zurich, June 6, 1961, only a few days before his eighty-sixth birthday.

Jung was successful in breaking down many barriers between psychiatry and religion. Religious and ethical problems, such as the hidden and continuous struggle between good and evil, held always an immense attraction for Jung. Much of his writing reflects his intense striving for a better and deeper understanding of these problems. Jung was not only a well-trained psychiatrist and psychologist, but he had an amazing knowledge of ancient and modern religions as well. Thus, with this vast knowledge, he was able to bring about a new and dynamic encounter between the psychological and the theological camps. The great moral problems which bear so closely on the destiny of Western civilization concerned Jung just as much as they have concerned any theologian.

At times Jung was called a philosopher and metaphysician. Jung objected to having these terms applied to him, for he looked upon himself as an empirical scientist. At Jung's funeral one of the speakers during the service referred to him as a great metaphysician. At that instant there was a tremendous clap of thunder. One of Jung's distinguished followers nudged another and said, "That was Professor Jung protesting that remark."

Nowhere in Jung's work is he more personally involved than when he deals with the relationship between man and God. I was not surprised upon visiting Jung's home to find engraved in stone above the doorway the Latin inscription, *Vocatus atque non vocatus Deus aberit.* "Invited, even not invited, God is present."

Jung objected to having his ideas classified and declared as part of a particular system of thought. Thus he would probably have resisted his concerns being categorized as existential. Yet he dealt with many of the themes common to existentialism. The shadow side of man's life, his cry for redemption and rebirth, his concern with death, anxiety, and guilt are given extensive discussion in Jung's works. Also his grappling therapeutically with the meaninglessness of life which confronted many of his patients points in this direction. In fact, Jung's special religious interests grew in part out of his work with patients extending over many years, and especially the fact that more than half of these patients were middle-aged and sought his advice because of a feeling of the pointlessness of their lives or lack of positive meaning, rather than because of a particular neurosis. Jung often remarked that these patients were quite well adapted to the ordinary tasks of life and had no special need to remake the pattern of their development. Their problem was to take it further.

Work with Schizophrenia

Among the many great contributions of Jung a few seem to stand out as especially applicable to present-day psychiatry. I particularly noticed, while on a World Health Organization travel fellowship during the summer of 1961, that, in the mental institutions of Switzerland, those psychiatrists who had been strongly influenced by Jung seemed to have some very special skills in the psychotherapeutic management of the schizophrenic patients which possibly other psychiatrists did not possess. Jung emphasized, even more than Freud, the understanding of symbolic language, and his followers have an amazingly vast knowledge of symbol and myth. This familiarity with symbolic language, along with Jung's deep concern for and interest in the schizophrenic patient, may account in part for the success of the Jungians in the treatment of schizophrenia.

I discussed this with C. A. Meier, the psychiatrist who not only succeeded Jung as professor of psychology at the Swiss Federal Institute of Technology, but who also enjoyed a lifelong association with him. Meier stated that in even the early stages of Jung's psychiatric career he was very interested in schizophrenia and was successful in treating a number of schizophrenic patients at the Burghölzli Hospital in Zurich. When Meier began his training there, Jung insisted that he work with schizophrenia, and Meier reports that he had three very genuine successes with chronic schizophrenic patients. Jung strongly encouraged Meier to analyze the schizophrenic patients and develop definitive methods of treatment and management. Meier remarked that Jung's interest in schizophrenia never faded. No matter what seminar he ever held he always brought up something about the understanding, treatment, and management of schizophrenia, and he encouraged a number of his students to work in this field. In Jung's private practice he had little opportunity to work with schizophrenic patients. Yet he encouraged others, and when he did have an opportunity to work with one, he readily accepted the challenge. An excellent summary of Jung's contributions to the theory and therapy of schizophrenia can be found in the Congress Report of the Second International Congress for Psychiatry which was held in Zurich, Switzerland, September, 1957.[2]

Another major contribution of Jung concerns itself with the understanding of the geriatric age group. Jung worked with many elderly patients and formulated some penetrating insights about the fears, concerns, and goals of these patients. With the rapid increase of the aged in our population his work in this area furnishes us with some valuable and valid guidelines for both treatment and research.

Jung's empirical method of psychological investigation led him to postulate an autonomous religious function in man. This was a strong antidote against Freud's atheism. It also opened up a new field of psychological research and a new era of interaction between psychiatry and religion. This particular area of Jung's work is of special interest today because of the religious problems, symbolism, and ideation which seem to be a part, large or small, of almost every psychiatric patient's illness. Thus, the psychotherapist is being forced to deal with these problems in the patient's treatment. If one studies the writings of Jung, he will find that Jung has already dealt validly with many of the

---

[2] This summary represents a paper presented by C. A. Meier and appears in Vol. 4, pp. 16-21, of the Congress Report.

religious problems raised by patients in the therapeutic situation.

Jung stressed the limitations of experimental psychology as a method of learning about the human psyche. In eloquent words he suggested more fruitful sources of information:

> Therefore anyone who wants to know the human psyche will learn next to nothing from experimental psychology. He would be better advised to put away his scholar's gown, bid farewell to his study, and wander with human heart through the world. There, in the horrors of prisons, lunatic asylums, and hospitals, in drab suburban pubs, in brothels and gambling-halls, in the salons of the elegant, the Stock Exchanges, Socialist meetings, churches, revivalist gatherings and ecstatic sects, through love and hate, through the experience of passion in every form in his own body, he would reap richer stores of knowledge than text-books a foot thick could give him, and he will know how to doctor the sick with real knowledge of the human soul.[3]

When he was asked, "When you have such an opportunity to see the seamy side of human nature, how is it that you still like folks?" he replied, "Because I have no illusions about them!" He knew the biological and the spiritual sides of man and accepted both.

Methodology

Jung followed throughout his life a very definite method in his work in the field of analytical psychology. It can be called a nonexperimental empirical method. He describes his methodological standpoint as exclusively phenomenological—"that is, it is concerned with occurrences, events, experiences, in a word, with facts." [4] He emphasized the difficulties inherent in psychological observation which grow out of the complex nature of the psychic phenomenon itself and the psychological observer's inevitable involvement in the phenomenon he is study-

[3] Jung, *Two Essays on Analytical Psychology*, tr. R. F. C. Hull (New York: Meridian Books, 1956), p. 258.
[4] Jung, *Psychology and Religion* (New Haven: Yale University Press, 1938), p. 3.

ing.[5] He wrote that the psychic phenomena with which he was concerned were all outside the experimental field and that the guinea pigs of experimental psychology, the chronoscopes, and cymographs were of no help to him. He went on to say that the psychologist's observations and his judgments all come from his own experience. Thus in this field every theory is ultimately a subjective personal statement.[6] Analytical psychology can therefore never be experimental except by sacrificing its very raison d'être, which is to study the psyche as a whole; however, Jung insists on the empirical nature of his science. The empirical method is concerned with giving an exact description of observed facts. When these facts are correlated, hypotheses can be established. Thus the aim behind Jung's empirical method remains the establishment of hypotheses. Jung did not use "hypothesis" to mean an unproven assumption. Raymond Hostie has described clearly Jung's use of this word:

An hypothesis is an intellectual insight made in response to certain demands, the one that at some particular point in the research affords the simplest, fullest and most likely explanation of all the facts under review. As such it is not simply a statement of fact, nor is it any final intellectual acquisition; it is simply an intellectual tool to help subsequent research, and therein lies its whole justification. As the science advances it can just as easily be cast away as preserved: this can only really be decided by the—unforeseeable—development of knowledge in the field in question.[7]

No hypothesis will ever be final, since it is essentially incomplete. Each can be modified, expanded, or abandoned. Thus Jung's work shows an endless series of fluctuations. His major aim is the establishment of scientific hypotheses on the basis of observed psychic facts.

One must understand Jung's use of the words "psychic

[5] Jung, *The Practice of Psychotherapy*, tr. R. F. C. Hull (London: Routledge and Kegan Paul, 1954).

[6] Jung, *The Structure and Dynamics of the Psyche*, tr. R. F. C. Hull (New York: Pantheon Books, 1960).

[7] Hostie, *Religion and the Psychology of Jung*, tr. G. R. Lamb (New York: Sheed and Ward, 1957), pp. 9-10.

reality" to avoid being confused. Anything that has an influence on the subject is real in a psychic sense. Jung would accept a physician's diagnosis that a patient is suffering from an imaginary cancer and therefore is in no need of a surgical operation. Jung would assert, however, that the cancer is a "psychic reality" for the patient and that the patient needs an "operation" of a psychological kind performed by a psychotherapist.[8] In his writings Jung often refers to psychic objects as being psychologically true. Since "true" is usually taken to be synonymous with "objective," many, such as Erich Fromm, have attacked this concept.[9] Thus "real" would seem to be a much more appropriate word than "true." Jung often stresses the point that God is a psychic reality, for when an idea is so old and generally believed, it must be true in some way—particularly *psychologically true*.[10]

While on one hand Jung emphasizes the special, specific nature of psychic realities, he hastens to insist that this tells us nothing either for or against the ultimate ontological reality of the things in question. At first Jung described psychic reality by reference to human consciousness. As his work developed he accepted Freud's concept of the unconscious as the "personal unconscious" but went on to describe a fundamental level common to all men which he designated as the collective unconscious. This collective unconscious is the product and container of man's ancestral history. The individual is born with many predispositions which have been bequeathed to him by his ancestors, and these predispositions will influence his conduct. Thus Jung contends that there is a collective personality which reaches out selectively into the world of experience and is modified and elaborated by the experiences which it receives.

The collective unconscious, usually designated today as the objective psyche, is the deepest layer of the unconscious. Its contents are called archetypes, and their manifestations are

---

[8] Jung, *Psychology and Religion*, pp. 2-14.

[9] Fromm, *Psychoanalysis and Religion* (New Haven: Yale University Press, 1950), pp. 15-17.

[10] Jung, *Answer to Job*, tr. R. F. C. Hull (New York: Meridian Books, 1954), p. 172; *Symbols of Transformation*, tr. R. F. C. Hull (New York: Pantheon Books, 1956), p. 7.

called archetypal images. The concept of the archetype is related to the concept of the instinct, in that an archetype is to the psyche what an instinct is to the body. An instinct is a pattern of behavior which is inborn and characteristic for a particular species. Jung taught that just as instincts common to a species are postulated by observing the uniformities in biological behavior, so archetypes are inferred by observing the uniformities in psychic phenomena. Archetypes are perceived and experienced subjectively through certain universal and recurring mythological motifs and images. These archetypal images, through symbolic elaboration, are the basic contents of myths, legends, fairy tales, and certain religions. Such images also emerge from the collective unconscious of individuals through dreams, profound subjective experience, or psychoses.

The hypothesis of a collective unconscious independent of the ego led Jung to postulate some higher instance able to synthesize the two elements of ego and unconscious. Jung named this power the *Selbst* or "self." He describes this term "on the one hand definite enough to convey the sum of human wholeness and on the other hand indefinite enough to express the indescribable and indeterminable nature of this wholeness." [11] He goes on to say that the "self" should be understood as the totality of the psyche and not only the center but also the whole circumference which embraces both conscious and unconscious, and that it is the center of this totality just as the ego is the center of the conscious mind.

Another methodological emphasis of Jung's is his distinction between a causal and a functional analysis. In a causal analysis everything is explained in terms of generally known principles of a simple nature, and such a method is reductive. In a functional analysis something is explained in terms of what it does or is striving to do—that is, what function it serves. Thus a causal analysis gives one a retrospective understanding while a functional analysis gives one a prospective understanding. Jung contends that a person is only half understood when one knows

[11] Jung, *Psychology and Alchemy*, tr. R. F. C. Hull (New York: Pantheon Books, 1953), p. 18.

how everything in him came about, for life is not made up of yesterdays only, nor is it understood or explained by reducing today to yesterday.

Life has also a to-morrow, and to-day is only understood if we are able to add the indications of to-morrow to our knowledge of what was yesterday. This holds good for all expressions of psychological life, even for symptoms of disease. Symptoms of neurosis are not merely consequences of causes that once have been, whether they were "infantile sexuality" or "infantile instinct for power." They are endeavours toward a new synthesis of life. It must immediately be added, however, they are endeavours that have miscarried. None the less they are attempts; they represent the germinal striving which has both meaning and value. They are embryos that failed to achieve life, owing to unpropitious conditions of an internal and external nature.[12]

Probably the most distinctive feature of Jung's view of man is that it combines teleology with causality and at this point differs strongly from Freud's theory of personality. Man's behavior is conditioned not just by his individual and racial history or past (causality) but also his aims, his aspiration, and where he is going (teleology). Thus the past as actuality and the future as potentiality guide one's present behavior. Jung's emphasis upon the role of destiny or purpose in human development sets him clearly apart from Freud. "For Freud, there is only the endless repetition of instinctual themes until death intervenes. For Jung, there is constant and often creative development, the search for wholeness and completion, and the yearning for rebirth." [13] Jung, moreover, emphasizes that the psychotherapist in his quest for understanding also has to be Janus-faced. He looks with one face into man's past, and with the other he looks into man's future; and the two views when combined yield a complete picture of man. "On the one side it [the mind] offers a picture

---

[12] Jung, *Collected Papers on Analytical Psychology*, tr. C. E. Long (2nd ed. London: Balliere, Tindall and Cox, 1920), pp. 385-95.
[13] C. S. Hall and G. Lindzey, *Theories of Personality* (New York: John Wiley & Sons, 1957), p. 78.

of the precipitate of the past, and on the other side a picture of the germinating knowledge of all that is to come, in so far as the psyche creates its own future." [14] Jung points out that solely a causal attitude is likely to produce resignation and despair in the individual, since from the standpoint of causality he is a prisoner of his past and cannot undo what has already been done. On the other hand, the teleological or finalistic attitude gives man a feeling of hope and something to live for.

Autonomous Religious Function

As I sat in the little community church of Kusnacht-Zurich, where students, colleagues, and friends had gathered for Jung's funeral on June 9, 1961, I found myself at the close of the service evaluating what had been said at this historic hour by the several distinguished speakers. It seemed that the most important words had been spoken by Jung's pastor when he stated that he agreed with Jung that the important dimension was not the particular church, sect, or doctrine to which one gave his allegiance; rather, it was one's own religious experience. C. A. Meier commented later on the great courage this pastor displayed by declaring Jung right in his emphasis when he (the pastor) belonged, of course, to a sectarian group.

Hans Schär, of Bern, in his address at Jung's funeral, spoke in a similar manner. He stated that in the center of Jung's work and thinking with regard to religion stands not the doctrine but the experience. Although perhaps simpler at times, it is more profound and more differentiated than the official church dogmas and doctrines, and binds and takes hold of the human much more readily, bringing him in touch with that which is real. Schär went on to say that because Jung took religious experience earnestly, he wrote *Answer to Job*, "that book which caused much attention and contradiction and which is understandable only to him who knows that in the living experience of God also the dark and abysmal God is experienced. He who knows that knows that such a book had to be written in our times."

[14] Jung, *Analytical Psychology* (New York: Moffat, Yard, 1916), chap. 13.

Jung's emphasis on the autonomous or authentic religious function in the unconscious mind stands as one of his greatest contributions to the understanding of the spiritual life of man. Jung has shown that the psyche possesses by nature a religious function and that it is the task of education to convey the archetype of the God-image, or its emanations and effects, to the conscious mind. "I have been accused of deifying the soul! I did not attribute a religious function to the soul, I merely produced the facts which prove that the soul is *naturaliter religiosa*, i.e., possesses a religious function." [15] Jung goes on to say that the religious point of view, understandably enough, puts the accent on the imprinter, whereas scientific psychology emphasizes the *typos*, the imprint. "The religious point of view understands the imprint as the working of an imprinter; the scientific point of view understands it as a symbol of an unknown and incomprehensible content." [16]

Freud often made the statement that he could not comprehend this phenomenon spoken of as religious experience.[17] Jung's words stand in sharp contrast with those of Freud when Jung declares that no matter what the world thinks about religious experience, the one who has it possesses the great treasure of a thing which has provided him with a source of life, meaning, and beauty. He goes on to ask where is the criterion by which one could say that such a life is not legitimate, that such an experience is not valid? "Is there, as a matter of fact, any better truth about ultimate things than the one that helps you to live? This is the reason why I take carefully into account the symbols produced by the unconscious mind." [18]

Jung contends that so long as religion is only faith and outward form and the religious function is not experienced in one's soul, nothing of any importance has happened. He goes on to say that it has yet to be understood that the *mysterium magnum* is not only an actuality but is first and foremost rooted in the

[15] Jung, *Psychology and Alchemy*, p. 13.
[16] *Ibid.*, p. 17.
[17] Freud, *Civilization and Its Discontents*, tr. Joan Riviere (New York: Jonathan Cape and Harrison Smith, 1930), pp. 7-22.
[18] Jung, *Psychology and Religion*, pp. 113-14.

human psyche. The man who does not know this from his own experience may be even a most learned theologian, but he has no idea of religion and still less of education.[19]

Some theologians are disappointed in Jung's concept of the autonomous religious function or instinct and feel that it is only a new version of the old medical materialism of William James. William James' concept, however, is that various religious phenomena are "nothing but" the effects of certain chemical changes in a person. As has already been shown, this is not Jung's idea, for when he speaks of a religious instinct innate in man, he is not referring to medical materialism. Jung's view is an ancient one. Even in Greek antiquity there was the belief that dreams are *somnia a deo missa*, that is, dreams sent by God. These ancients held the idea that man's soul or his unconscious serves, under certain conditions, as a door through which the divine or religious element is capable of reaching his conscious mind, and this view has actually always been believed. If a man's soul has a divine spark in it and is, as the Scriptures record, made in the image of God, and if it participates in any way in the realm which transcends the conscious self, it is a ready-made instrument for that purpose. Jung made the famous statement that he had never really cured a patient in the second half of life unless, in the course of the treatment, that person found access to the religious function. This statement grew out of Jung's vast clinical experience, and we ought to take it seriously. Ministers, however, have often abused this statement and interpreted it as meaning that unless a patient joins some particular church and becomes active as a church member, he cannot be healed. This is not Jung's meaning. Jung simply means that one has to come to grips with the religious function or instinct within himself. Thus, in regard to this innate religious function, Jung's view is very different from that of Freud, for there is no room in the Freudian system for an autonomous religious function.

In Freud's *Civilization and Its Discontents*, which he pub-

---

[19] Jung, *Psychology and Alchemy*, p. 13.

lished in 1930, he discusses in the opening chapter a letter from a close friend. Freud had sent this friend a copy of his *Future of an Illusion*, which was published three years earlier. The friend was writing to tell Freud that although he agreed with his views on religion, he was sorry that Freud had not properly appreciated the ultimate source of religious sentiments. This consisted in a peculiar feeling, which never left him personally, which he found shared by many others, and which he supposed millions more also experienced. Freud goes on to describe the content of his friend's correspondence:

It is a feeling which he would like to call a sensation of "eternity," a feeling as of something limitless, unbounded, something "oceanic." It is, he says, a purely subjective experience, not an article of belief; it implies no assurance of personal immortality, but it is the source of the religious spirit and is taken hold of by the various churches and religious systems, directed by them into definite channels and also, no doubt, used up in them. One may rightly call oneself religious on the ground of this oceanic feeling alone, even though one reject all beliefs and all illusions.[20]

Freud expressed his inability to deal scientifically with feelings and also declared that he could not discover this oceanic feeling in himself. He attempted a genetic explanation of such a feeling and postulated that the oceanic feeling sought to reinstate the limitless narcissism of early childhood.

Thus religious experience was not an understandable phenomenon for Freud in the sense that it was for Jung. Freud was criticized for confining his discussion to the beliefs of the common man and ignoring the rarer and more profound types of religious emotion experienced by mystics and saints. Freud admitted this omission in his exposition and justified it by remarking that he was concerned primarily with what religion signified to humanity in general.[21] In a publication eight years later, *Moses and Monotheism*, Freud remedied this omission by dis-

---

[20] Freud, *Civilization and Its Discontents*, p. 8.
[21] *Ibid.*, p. 23.

cussing the question as to how it is that religious emotion attains a greater sublimity, profundity, and majesty than any other human emotion. He continued, however, to be reductive in his explanation. Possibly he was saying that as a psychologist his province was to show that much in religion could be accounted for by the psychological and historical factors he had investigated, so that he personally could see no reason for adding to them an external supernatural one.

It would be difficult to spend any time at the Jung Institute without doing some serious thinking about the meaning of religious experience. One of the most fruitless discussions indulged in today by theologians and psychiatrists is whether the religious experience of a particular individual is normal or pathological. Why should any genuine religious experience be looked upon as pathological? Why cannot any valid religious experience be considered as normal? The reaction to the experience can be either normal or pathological, and this is what should be emphasized. The great saint is honored because of the validity of his religious experience, whereas the catatonic schizophrenic in a mental institution who stands frozen with an ecstatic expression on his face lifted toward the sky is looked upon as having had a pathological religious experience. The religious experience of the saint and that of the person in the mental institution may be the same. The reaction of the saintly person was normal, and the reaction of the schizophrenic to his religious experience was, of course, pathological. The difference seems to be in ego strength. The strong person feels overcome by the presence of Christ within him, and he feels that he is becoming Christ or Christlike. He begins to think that possibly he is losing his mind, but then decides that this is too wonderful a thing to fall in the category of insanity, and he begins to evaluate himself and possibly to search the Scriptures for an understanding of his religious experience. Possibly he then runs across a statement such as that made by Paul, ". . . yet not I, but Christ liveth in me" (Gal. 2:20). Then he begins to integrate and fit the experience into his life. He is able to contain himself, for his head and his heart are strong enough to encompass this religious experience. On the other hand, the person with a somewhat weak ego feels the impact of such a religious experience and immediately declares that he is Jesus Christ. He is overwhelmed by the experience, and his head and heart are too small to contain the experience. He becomes either a babbling idiot, declaring himself God, or frozen into a catatonic state with an expression of ecstasy on his face. The impact of a genuinely deep religious experience is almost always overwhelming. The whole history of man's encounter with God points this out. Time and again the prophets avoided hearing the voice of God, seeing him, or letting him get hold of them in any way, because they were afraid they could not contain themselves after such an encounter. This is illustrated beautifully in the biblical books of Isaiah and Jeremiah.

Jung discusses this same theme in *Two Essays on Analytical Psychology* and begins his discussion by comparing an experience of a mentally ill man with that of Schopenhauer, showing how the experience of one led to inflation and disintegration and the other to integration and wholeness.[22]

Some of the students at the Jung Institute, in discussing religious experience, commented on the teachings of certain of the churches in regard to this phenomenon. As for the Protestants, their approach is intellectual and a rational one. They teach that by searching the Scriptures, and through the proper interpretation of the Word, one finds or has a religious experience. These students went on to say that the Roman Catholics teach that the religious experience comes only through the church and its sacraments and teachings. In other words, the church is the vessel that contains the religious experience and those who get it must get it from drinking from this particular vessel. Thus it is very upsetting to some churchmen to think that one might find God while lying on the couch of a psychoanalyst. However, if theologians approach the matter from the standpoint of Carl Jung and see in man an autonomous religious function, then they would realize that man can come face to face

[22] Tr. R. F. C. Hull (New York: Meridian Books, 1956), pp. 153-65.

with God without having any relationship to an organized church, in the same way he has done in the past before the advent of the church. When one can, at least, understand this point of view, he sees more clearly than ever why Jung took the statement of Tertullian, the early church father, who said "Man is naturally Christian," and changed it to "man is naturally religious."

The Separation of Conscious from Unconscious

Jung and his followers stress that modern man is cut off from his unconscious, the major source of his healing. Symbols no longer have much meaning for him, although they are alive in his unconscious. "The educated public, the flower of our actual civilization, has lifted itself up from its roots and is about to lose its connections with the earth." [23] From the philosophical point of view man today is very much a product of the humanism of the eighteenth-century Enlightenment movement and of nineteenth-century reductive naturalism. Jung was deeply concerned with the historical process of the despiritualization of the world —the withdrawal of projections—which meant that everything of a divine or demonic character must return to the soul, to the inside of the unknown man. Thus it is easy to conclude that since the throne of God could not be discovered among the galactic systems, the inference was that God never existed. Often when man declares his God dead or nonexistent, he then declares himself a god. This type of inflation may result in a psychological disturbance in the form of a dissociation of personality. Or the energy once invested in an existence as great as God reappears under another name which one might call the "state" or an "ism" of which people believe, hope, and expect as much as they formerly did of God. Jung points out also that from a social point of view, when people lose the idea of God, "the masses begin to breed mental epidemics, of which we have now a fair number." [24]

[23] Jung, *Psychology and Religion*, p. 95.
[24] *Ibid.*, p. 105.

Once, in talking with F. Riklin, president of the Curatorium of the Jung Institute, Zurich, regarding Jung's ideas of how much in modern society tends to fragment man rather than heal him, Dr. Riklin pointed out how often even in psychotherapy we impose on patients our ideas and directions which we feel they need (or ought to need) without enough concern for what the patient really needs. The end result is that the psychotherapist has not assisted in healing but has contributed to illness. Then he related an interesting story of a missionary from Africa who visited him recently to discuss a similar error he felt his church was making. He came to persuade the Jung Institute to send some Jungian psychoanalysts to Africa in the area where he worked to help the Africans reestablish their roots with their great past, which had been disrupted by the white man through his business and missionary enterprises. No analysts were available for this. Then the possibility of sending some Africans to the Jung Institute to get some training was considered. That did not become a reality either.

This missionary told Dr. Riklin the following story. His missionary group had been able to convert to Christianity a chief of a prominent African tribe. Shortly after his conversion he called at the missionary station and told the workers there that he had had a vision of Christ. They told him that was fine and asked what Christ had said to him. The chief replied, "He said, 'I bless you.'" The missionaries were pleased with the chief's experience and expressed to him their approval. Then they went on to tell the chief that since he had three wives, he must give up two of them. He very painfully surrendered his two younger wives and kept the older one. Shortly thereafter he became completely psychotic. The missionaries were very upset about this, for Christianity was at stake in the tribe and, therefore, they had to help heal this man. There were no mental institutions to which this African chief might be sent, so they decided to take care of him themselves. They always kept one of the missionaries or workers from the mission station in the tent with the chief to watch over him. They took turns, each one staying for about a month. This was very trying for the busy missionaries, for their station was small, yet they felt they had no choice. No matter what they did the chief did not seem to recover. About a year and a half passed. Finally they had exhausted almost all the workers at the mission station, and then sent down to the tent of the chief a rather simple white man who worked at the station. He stayed with the chief much longer than the others, possibly about two months. While he was there, he fell in love with one of the black native girls. He could not leave the tent of the chief because he had to watch over him, therefore he courted and had sexual relations with this black girl in the presence of the chief. Almost immediately thereafter the chief became well.

Dr. Riklin said the missionary had no explanation for what had happened, in that the chief was cured after the white man from the missionary station had sexual relations with one of the black native women. Dr. Riklin suggested an explanation. The experience had reestablished the connection between the chief and his unconscious, and he was no longer fragmented but made whole again. Dr. Riklin said that he told the missionary that when Christ appeared to this chief, he said nothing to him about giving up his two wives but that he blessed him with his three wives and did not mention that he should surrender any of them. Therefore, the missionaries had imposed upon this man something that had not been imposed upon him by his encounter with Christ. He was made ill by having imposed upon him something which was artificial and foreign, which he could not understand, and which also separated him from his instinctual nature, his unconscious, his source of healing.

This story is suggestive of a major theme in much of Laurens van der Post's writings on Africa. He emphasizes that we have broken in upon the Negro and disturbed his intuitive and instinctual life, where once his primary bonds to nature were very strong. The white man has let him taste of the fruit of knowledge, and he has begun to take on the white man's thoughts, hopes, and way of life. His own way of life has been disturbed or destroyed, so he cannot return to that, yet his entry into the white man's way of life is blocked by the white man.[25] Van der Post and the missionary who came to Zurich to see Dr. Riklin seem to be saying essentially the same thing.

Jung has dealt beautifully with this theme in *The Undiscovered Self*.

Nothing estranges man more from the ground plan of his instincts than his learning capacity, which turns out to be a genuine drive toward progressive transformations of human modes of behavior. It, more than anything else, is responsible for the altered conditions of our existence and the need for new adaptations which civilization brings. It is also the source of numerous psychic disturbances and difficulties occasioned by man's progressive alienation from his instinctual foundation, i.e., by his uprootedness and identification with his conscious knowledge of himself, by his concern with consciousness at the expense of unconscious.[26]

Jung goes on to say that the result is that modern man can know himself only insofar as he can become conscious of himself. His consciousness orients itself chiefly by observing and investigating the world around him. In the process of this adaption he loses sight of his instinctual nature and puts his own conception of himself in place of his real being. Jung believes that separation from his instinctual nature inevitably plunges civilized man into the conflict between conscious and unconscious, spirit and nature, knowledge and faith, a split that becomes pathological the moment his consciousness is no longer able to neglect or suppress his instinctual side. Groups of such individuals often start mass movements, purporting to be the champions of the suppressed.

In accordance with the prevailing tendency of consciousness to seek the source of all ills in the outside world, the cry goes up for political and social changes which, it is supposed, would automatically solve the much deeper problem of split personality. Hence it is

[25] Laurens van der Post, *The Dark Eye in Africa* (New York: William Morrow & Co., 1955).
[26] Tr. R. F. C. Hull (New York: The New American Library, 1959), p. 92.

that whenever this demand is fulfilled, political and social conditions arise which bring the same ills back again in altered form.[27]

Many theologians, such as Paul Tillich and Samuel H. Miller of Harvard, have spoken and written of how the great symbols are not meaningful today. These symbols are ancient, embedded in the unconscious, and are a part of the myth, folklore, and fairy tales of people. These symbols are very much alive in the unconscious, but modern man is cut off from his unconscious, and his symbols will live again only through a deeper understanding of unconscious material. His life is encompassed by the humanism of the eighteenth-century Enlightenment movement and also nineteenth-century reductive naturalism. Allegiance to this type of materialistic philosophy cuts one off from his unconscious, and thus his symbols seem dead. The Jungians feel that ministers could interpret anew these symbols and help revive their meaning through the proper type of preaching and in the worship of the church. Possibly the ministers hesitate to do this because they are afraid of what will happen if these symbols become alive again. The religious awakening could possibly be too great for the present church to contain it. One of the faculty members of the Jung Institute, in discussing such a religious awakening, mentioned that Jung often decried the failure of ministers to preach on the topic of the Holy Spirit. One rarely hears the topic discussed, and when one does, it is presented in a confusing and muddling manner. In the early church the Holy Spirit existed as the true *Spiritus Veritas*, the continuing revelation of God, the continuing encounter of God with man. Jung was quoted as saying that if one listens to theologians he will decide that God stopped "publishing" in A.D. 32 and has never communicated anything to man since then.

Conclusion

Jung's name is always mentioned as one of the big three of early dynamic psychology, and every textbook has a brief state-

[27] *Ibid.*, pp. 93-94.

ment about him. The average student in psychiatry, however, is given very few lectures on Jung and has done little reading of Jung's works. The general impression is that Jung's writings are almost incomprehensible and, therefore, if one should study Jung, he should read interpretations of Jung's works. Although Jung is often difficult to understand, he has written much which is very comprehensible. Also, most of what he has written is easier to understand than the writings about him. A sad thing to contemplate is that Jung has already dealt validly with many problems which are disturbing mankind, but he has not been heard. His rejection in many circles may prove to be one of the tragic accidents of history.

Jung was indeed one of the outstanding figures in the religious history of this century. Although people of many religious persuasions gathered around him, Jung explicitly declared his allegiance to Christianity. Some of the most important of his works deal with the religious problems of the Christian. He studied these religious problems from the standpoint of psychology and not from the approach of theology. In his work he stressed the necessity of understanding and reflecting, as against the Christian demand for faith. Thus out of his clinical and empirical observations came many rich insights about religion. His secretary, Aniela Jaffé, reported that Jung wrote to a young clergyman in 1952: "I find that all my thoughts circle around God like the planets around the sun, and are as irresistibly attracted by Him. I would feel it to be the grossest sin if I were to oppose any resistance to this force."

His splendid autobiography, entitled *Memories, Dreams, Reflections*, published since his death, is essentially a record of his inner experiences. Jung's exciting and searching story of his spiritual journey will set many individuals on the path of self-discovery.

While his work in psychoanalysis and the science of the mind stands as his most important achievement, his contributions to certain aspects of world thinking are far greater than those of other leaders in psychology and psychiatry. He was a brilliant student. His depth of understanding and his vast knowledge in countless fields almost stagger the imagination. Through exploration of ancient myths, primitive folklore, comparative religions, and a wide range of contemporary cultures Jung sought out the basic themes and built a comprehensive philosophy of life and death. He urged for the individual wholeness, and this included realization of all his potentials, awareness of depth and purpose in life, and harmony between his inner and outer worlds. Mankind's quest for self-understanding has been immeasurably enriched by Jung's genius. It is predicted that his impact on history will increase with each passing year.

5

Freud and Calvin:
A Comparative Study

C. Macfie Campbell, the Scotchman who was director of the Boston Psychopathic Hospital and professor of psychiatry at Harvard University School of Medicine from 1920 to his death in 1943, once said that philosophically speaking, psychoanalysis is Calvinism in Bermuda shorts. The definitive nature of this striking statement suggests a comparative discussion. In considering the concepts and ideas, the attitudes and habits of the two personalities begetting these respective "religions," remarkable similarities emerge, evidencing the true philosophic parallelism of Sigmund Freud and John Calvin.

A point of interest is Freud's admiration for Oliver Cromwell, the great Puritan commander who adhered to the Calvinist dogma. In fact, Freud named a son after Oliver Cromwell. Philip Rieff, in *Freud: The Mind of a Moralist*, says that the affinity for militant puritanism, not uncommon among secular Jewish intellectuals, indicates a certain preferred character type, starched with independence and cerebral rectitude rather than with a particular belief or doctrine.[1]

Ascetic Tendencies

Both Freud and Calvin had ascetic tendencies. For the hedonistic outlook Calvin had the utmost scorn. Many of his invectives against the libertines are ablaze with denunciations of the pleasure-seeking attitude. Nevertheless, we are not to make ourselves miserable in this life, for it would be insulting God to refuse to use the gifts he offers. According to Calvin we are

[1] (New York: The Viking Press, 1959).

ever to remember that this life is but a pilgrimage to the life beyond, where lies our true felicity.

Calvin believed that sex could be harnessed and set to constructive uses. His attempts at controlling the sexual drives led him into moralism and legalism, the parents of prudery. He taught that sex is not to be enjoyed, even in marriage, but kept within the rigid bounds of delicacy and propriety. Calvin, however, did possess some understanding of the importance of sex in life. He was not convinced that sex was good, but realized that it was inevitable. He failed to appreciate sex as a means of expressing conjugal love or of symbolizing physically a union of two personalities. Procreation remained for Calvin, as for Augustine and Aquinas, the only really positive purpose of sex. He did not accept sex as the natural gift of God and any pleasure derived from it was sullied, though God "draws the veil of holy matrimony over it."

Calvin opposed many forms of enjoyment now generally recognized as wholesome. Frugality and simplicity took an ascetic turn. He was staunchly opposed to dancing and the theater. Card playing could be permitted only with certain rigid reservations. Instrumental music was banned from the churches. Songs had to pass the censor. He suggested that churches and dwellings be plainly furnished. Calvin did not want any of the gifts of God abused, so the only safe course was to eschew all vain display. He felt that since this life is a preparation for the next, we are pilgrims traveling toward another land. While we are still on the earth we must endure patiently its trials and keep our souls uncorrupted by the vain pleasures of the world.

Freud lived a rather ascetic and inhibited life in many ways. He is often accused of advocating uninhibited self-indulgence. However, he advocated promiscuous indulgences in sex no more than he did promiscuous indulgences in eating. Anita Loos understood Freud in this respect. In the frank "diary" of Lorelei Lee's predatory love life, *Gentlemen Prefer Blondes*, Miss Loos describes a conference with Freud. Lorelei went to Freud, hoping for psychoanalysis, but received the advice that she use some suppression instead:

So yesterday he took me to Dr. Froyd. So Dr. Froyd and I had quite a long talk in the english landguage. So it seems that everybody seems to have a thing called inhibitions, which is when you want to do a thing and you do not do it. So then you dream about it instead. So Dr. Froyd asked me, what I seemed to dream about. So I told him that I never really dream about anything. I mean I use my brains so much in the day time that at night they do not seem to do anything else but rest. So Dr. Froyd was very very surprized at a girl who did not dream about anything. So then he asked me all about my life. I mean he was very very sympathetic, and he seems to know how to draw a girl out quite a lot. I mean I told him things that I really would not even put in my diary. So then he seemed very very intreeged at a girl who always seemed to do everything she wanted to do. So he asked me if I really never wanted to do a thing that I did not do. For instance did I ever want to do a thing that was really violent, for instance did I ever want to shoot someone for instance. So then I said I had. . . . So then Dr. Froyd looked at me and looked at me and he said he did not really think it was possible. . . . So then Dr. Froyd said that all I needed was to cultivate a few inhibitions and get some sleep.[2]

Freud's biographer, Ernest Jones, points out that it is likely that the more passionate side of life subsided with Freud earlier than it does with many men.[3] Freud, at forty-one, wrote to his friend Wilhelm Fliess, complaining about his moods and then adding, "Also sexual excitation is of no more use to a person like me." Another incident points to the fact that around this age his sexual life had more or less ended. He reports, in *The Interpretation of Dreams*, that at one time, in his forties, he felt physically attracted to a young woman and half-voluntarily touched her slightly.[4] He comments on how surprised he was to "still" find the possibility for such attraction to him.

[2] From *Gentlemen Prefer Blondes* by Anita Loos. By permission of Liveright Publishers, New York. Copyright © renewed 1953 by Anita Loos.

[3] Jones, *The Life and Work of Sigmund Freud* (New York: Basic Books, 1955), Vol. II.

[4] Freud, *The Interpretation of Dreams*, tr. James Strachey (London: Allen & Unwin, 1955).

In searching through Freud's writings one can find considerable evidence that his views about sex, and especially the remarks about his own sexual life, were the rationalizing expression of his inhibited sexuality. It has been reported that Freud gave up sex in his forties. He himself said, "I stand for an infinitely freer sexual life, although I myself have made very little use of such freedom." Actually, Freud, the great spokesman for sex, was a typical puritan. To him, the aim of life for a civilized individual was to suppress his emotional and sexual impulses and, at the expense of this suppression, to lead a civilized life. The uncivilized mob is not capable of such sacrifice. In contrast to the mob are the intellectual elite who are capable of not satisfying their impulses and sublimating them for higher purposes. Thus, civilization is the result of such nonsatisfaction of instinctual impulses.

Freud's life has often been compared with that of Goethe, although he lived a much simpler life than Goethe. When Freud was asked to write his autobiography, what he wrote was actually a brief history of the psychoanalytic movement. All of his life he lived quietly with and within the circle of his family. To this family circle were added several devoted friends, mostly pioneers in psychoanalysis.

Although Freud proclaimed that sex was natural, that procreation was secondary to pleasure, and that society should not hold too severe restrictions on sexual instincts, he was still a Victorian. He was not the romanticist he has at times been called. He was the rationalist who approved of the stern conscience. Naming his faith logos and eros, he sought to bring the irrational, primitive side of human nature under the disciplined control of reason. He felt that when sex plays its proper, ordered role in the total pattern of the personality, it can contribute to physical and emotional health.

Work

Both Calvin and Freud were compulsive in their work habits. The lifetime accomplishments of each are so great that they almost stagger the imagination.

Calvin was an unusually hardworking person who prized high-ly the virtue of industry. He taught that it pleases God that men should work, each one in the estate to which he has been called. Nothing is more unseemly than a man who is idle and good-for-nothing. Calvin's condemnation of idleness appears most plainly in conjunction with Paul's rule that "if any would not work, neither should he eat." Man was created to do some-thing. Idleness was not to be encouraged by supplying the lazy with food. Although Calvin enjoined almsgiving as a religious duty, he warned against the feeding of the shiftless. Work be-came idealized and a road to accomplishment and distinction, rather than a drudgery to expiate the pressing sense of guilt or a God-inflicted punishment. In early Christianity the beggar could be God's child, a successful penitent, or even glorified as a saint. In Calvin's acquisitive status society the attitude toward the beggar was simply, "He ought to be ashamed."

It is more in Calvin's example than in his precepts that we find his most potent influence regarding work. He labored in-cessantly and in the face of many obstacles. In spite of ill health he did an amazing amount of work. His writings in the fifty-nine volumes of the *Opera* constitute a literary output which few men could have equaled, even if they had done nothing else. He spent time lecturing and preaching—nearly five hun-dred engagements a year—counseling those in need, admon-ishing offenders, and fighting his way through incessant contro-versies of the first twenty years of his ministry. The Swiss give him credit for helping to establish in Switzerland the watch industry, the banking business, and the public school system. His accomplishments testify to astounding industry.

Freud, when asked what he considered the ultimate in nor-mality, replied: *"Arbeiten und lieben"*—to work and to love. This devotion to work, to unremitting creative effort, was a part of his concept of normalcy or health. He severely indicts the laziness of the masses. He makes only a few references to the medicinal necessity of work, although it is negatively urged by his regular disparagements of public and private fantasy, whether in dreams, neurotic withdrawal, or ethical utopianism. In his book *The Future of an Illusion* the theme is overt. He declares that men must work and makes it a test of maturity and independence. The fact that "men are not naturally fond of work" and that "arguments are of no avail against their passions" establishes "two widely diffused human characteristics" which make a coercive society inevitable.[5]

As with Calvin, it is more in Freud's productivity than in his precepts that we discover his attitude toward work. His numerous books and papers, extensive lecturing, wide correspondence, heavy treatment schedule of patients, and leadership in organizing and nurturing the psychoanalytic movement furnish the evidence for a life that was never idle. He suffered for many years from a severe, progressive ailment which destroyed a large part of his jawbone. He was operated upon several times. He needed constant expert surgical supervision and suffered a considerable amount of pain. In spite of this physical pain he continued to work.

Religion

Both Calvin and Freud were consumed by their interest in religion. In general, however, Freud's view was negative and Calvin's positive. More of Freud's writings deal with religion than with any other subject except the theory and practice of psychoanalysis as a form of therapy.

Calvin's total life was involved in religion. He looked upon himself as God's prosecuting attorney in the celestial battle against unrighteousness. He permitted no deviation from what he considered the true doctrine. Possibly his bigoted certainty prompted his insistence that everybody agree with him, in an effort to strengthen his faith. Thus, his unconscious need to rebel and to doubt God would never reach his consciousness.

Concept of God

Freud charged that Christianity's father image was not sufficiently strict and demanding. In *The Future of an Illusion*

---

[5] Tr. W. D. Robson-Scott (Garden City, N. Y.: Doubleday & Co., 1957).

he questioned the "kindness" of the Christian God, who "must lay a restraining hand upon his justice. One sinned, and then one made oblation or did penance, and then one was free to sin anew." He commented that Moses, the creator of the Jews, was neither kindly nor indulgent. Thus, Freud's God was the strong, patriarchal, judgmental, and masculine figure.

Calvin's concept was similar. He was concerned with the practical question of how to live in obedience to the will of God. Unlike Jesus, Calvin conceived the will of God in terms of biblical literalism and set up a legalistic moral code. Calvin's ethic rested on his bedrock conviction of the absolute and final authority of the will and Word of God. He believed in the absolute sovereignty of God; it was foolish and impious to ask a reason for God's action.

Thus, both Freud and Calvin viewed religion as patriarchal and father-centered. Carl Jung has emphasized repeatedly in his writings that Protestantism is too father-centered, with the mother principle left out. Jung points out that the Roman Catholic Church has kept alive and nurtured the feminine principle or mother through the dogmas related to the Blessed Virgin.

Concept of Man

Calvin stressed man's utter depravity and sinfulness. He emphasized the doctrine of original sin. Adam's sin had tainted the whole human race and robbed man of his goodness. Thus, because of this corruption, man was a child of evil. In some ways the original sin concept can be compared to Freud's concept of the id. Freud emphasized the strong biological and instinctual impulses of man as really being the controlling life force. Thus, there appears to be considerable similarity between Freud's concept of the id and Calvin's concept of original sin.

In one of Freud's letters he wrote: "In the depths of my heart I can't help being convinced that my dear fellow men, with a few exceptions, are worthless." This pessimism about man is repeatedly emphasized in *The Future of an Illusion*.

Concept of Life

Actions as Symptoms. Calvin, with his doctrine of predestination, turned all action into symptom. In the Calvinistic system nobody can say with absolute certainty whether or not another is of the elect, for the invisible church of the elect does not coincide with the visible church. A careful scrutiny of the outer actions could give a hint of the inner condition as one of grace or damnation. Thus, a man may reveal his election by the quality of his works. According to Calvin, good works can never save a man, but good works may be a sign that God has saved him. One who feels himself chosen wants to give external evidence of it. Thus, the Calvinist labors with untiring zeal to "make his calling and election sure."

When Freud analyzed all actions symptomatically, the greatest interest in his work came from those persons nurtured as well as troubled in cultures which were Calvinistic or otherwise rigorously ascetic. Thus, the therapeutic of the psychological age is successor to the ascetic of the religious age. In the age of psychological man the hope of deciphering God's decision and design for one's life is not so intense as in Calvin's day. The Calvinist probably finds considerable relief in the decreased emphasis of this tenet of his faith. However, Freudianism and Calvinism do share the passion for acquiring some knowledge of one's personal destiny.

To psychological man today, as well as to the ascetic of Calvin's day, all destinies are intensely personal.[6] The way to this self-knowledge is and was to trace back a person's conduct from symptom to the inner conditions responsible for the symptom. In the religious period the symptom was called sin. The task of the clergy was to make the sinner aware of his sin, so that he would be self-convicted. The psychoanalyst makes the neurotic therapeutically aware of his neurosis. The neurotic, like his predecessor the sinner, is reluctant to admit his weakness. This failure to admit a fundamental weakness is the most obvious

⁶ Philip Rieff, "The American Transference: From Calvin to Freud," *The Atlantic Monthly*, July, 1961.

characteristic of the inner wrong which the sinner and neurotic commit against themselves. Thus, Calvin's pastors and Freud's analysts had the difficult and thankless task of educating for that state of awareness. The admission of weakness is the beginning of emotional or spiritual strength in both the religious and the psychotherapeutic traditions.

The similar approaches of Calvinism and Freudianism in handling the sinner and neurotic have caused considerable concern in such individuals as O. Hobart Mowrer, research professor of psychology, University of Illinois. He feels that today there is an unholy alliance between Calvinism and Freudianism, and that man's problem stems from a repressed superego rather than a repressed id. Thus, the people we are calling neurotics are really sinners. People get sick because they are sinful and not because they are too moral. They are not moral enough. They have violated their moral natures. Mowrer is disturbed that the church has accepted Freudianism to the extent that what was once condemned is now basking in the sunlight of this apostolic blessing.[7] Perhaps the many features which Calvinism and Freudianism hold in common made it inevitable that they would embrace each other.

Today, in our culture, there is an acute sense of the weakness of human character but a diminished capacity to feel compassion for weakness. Devices of release from the tension of trying to be good or successful remain operative in Roman Catholic cultures, but have withered away in the ascetic tradition of Calvinism. Probably because of this, psychoanalytic therapy has not found as ready and receptive an audience in those areas of Western culture that remain Roman Catholic. Philip Rieff discusses this lucidly in an article which appeared in *The Atlantic Monthly:*

Meanwhile, in those parts of the ascetic West that had lost their religious impetus, the contempt for weakness, inherent anyway in Calvinist doctrine, grew steadily more powerful. The individual,

[7] *The Crisis in Religion and Psychiatry* (Princeton, N.J.: D. Van Nostrand Co., 1961).

caught in this hard, dying culture, tried to hide his sense of weakness, for he no longer felt a compelling explanation for it; nor could he use something in his system of worship to escape this now intensely personal fault (no longer attributable to divine decision). The culture, always guilt-ridden, was no longer guilt-releasing. Without the remedy of grace or good works, conscience became the seat of emotional weakness rather than the sign of moral strength.[8]

Predestination and Determinism. Calvin and Freud share a common view regarding the bondage of man to forces outside his control. For Calvin this is his doctrine of predestination; for Freud, his theory of psychic determinism.

Calvin believed in the absolute sovereignty of God. Since God is all-powerful, he determines every act. Since he is all-wise, he foreknows and predetermines every detail of human history. If one says that some achieve salvation through their own initiative, he is placing limits on the divine sovereignty, and such an inconsistency Calvin rejects with inexorable logic. Since some appear to be saved and some to be damned, the only explanation consistent with the absolute sovereignty of God is to say that God elects some for salvation and others for eternal punishment.

There seems to be an irreconcilable conflict between Calvin's doctrine of God's absolute sovereignty and man's responsibility. If one is to be held responsible, he must be free. If one is not to be blamed for that which he cannot help, the predestination doctrine leaves little ground for blame. Astonishingly, though, Calvinism calls men to account for their sins more profoundly than any other form of theological belief. Calvin did not reconcile this conflict, although he fully believed that he had. He was diligent in his efforts to reform mankind.

It is generally conceded that psychoanalysis as a theoretical system is a firm believer in determinism. The most fundamental and most significant of Freud's findings are his doctrines that psychic processes are strictly determined, that actions and feel-

[8] Rieff, *op. cit.,* p. 107.

ings may be determined by unconscious motivations, and that the motivations driving us are emotional forces.

The working hypothesis that psychic processes are as strictly determined as physical processes permitted the tackling of psychic manifestations, such as dreams, fantasies, and errors of everyday life, which had hitherto been regarded as incidental, meaningless, or mysterious. It also led to a psychological understanding of phenomena which formerly had been ascribed to organic stimuli: for example, the psychic foundation of anxiety dreams, the psychic consequences of masturbation, the psychic determination of hysteria, the psychic determinants of functional diseases, and exhaustion through work. This concept of determinism permitted a constructive approach to occurrences which until then had been attributed to external factors and hence had not aroused psychological interests, such as the psychic factors involved in incurring accidents, motivation for the formation and retention of certain habits, the psychic understanding of repetitive experiences previously attributed to fate. The doctrine that psychic processes are determined is one of the premises without which the psychoanalyst could not take a single step in his daily analytical work.

One should never forget that in spite of Freud's deterministic viewpoint and his great emphasis on the past as the conditioner of the future, he involved himself in the treatment of patients with the intention of liberating them, at least in part, from the bondage of the past. Thus, no matter what might have been his theories, in practice he accepted man's capacity to change, thereby acknowledging the existence of freedom in man. If one fails to recognize this freedom, he could surely not in good faith participate in psychotherapy either as therapist or as patient.

Heresy

Both Calvin and Freud insisted on the purity of doctrine, and those who deviated from the true faith were punished and excluded from among the faithful.

Calvin punished heretics, and Calvinists after him punished heretics. For the Calvinists, religion could not be a matter of private interpretation. It was the duty of the elect to enforce purity of faith in the community by any disciplinary measures that might prove necessary. They regarded the doctrine of Calvin's *Institutes* as absolute truth and the supreme moral criterion. If man suffered in the process, that was regrettable. Yet charity must be subservient to purity of faith. "We must not offend God for the love of our neighbor." Thus, Calvin played a major role in having the great theologian and physician, Servetus, burned at the stake. This was especially a great loss to medicine, for Servetus had discovered the pulmonary circulation of the blood in 1546, three quarters of a century before William Harvey. Many others in Geneva received various punishments or were expelled from the church. The tradition continued in the execution of the Quakers who were hanged for heresy on Boston Common. The thirteenth chapter of Deuteronomy was Calvin's justification for a substantial part of his theory of the duty of exterminating heretics. Calvin found biblical justification for ruthlessness in stamping out enemies of God. The Old Testament furnished him a treasure-house of such instances. Calvin's theory of persecution grew out of the conviction that because God's will is inviolable, the elect must be his instruments to crush apostasy and defeat the wiles of Satan.

The psychoanalytic movement has dealt with heresy and often in a not too dissimilar way from that of Calvinism. Many members of the early psychoanalytic circle were excluded from the group because of deviations of one kind or another from the purity of the doctrine. Some of those excluded were Eli Bernays, Josef Breuer, Theodor Meynert, Carl Jung, Alfred Adler, Wilhelm Fliess, Sandor Ferenczi, Otto Rank, Fritz Wittels, and Wilhelm Stekel. Several times in Freud's writings he mentions his need for a loved friend and a hated enemy. He seemed to have the capacity to love and hate passionately, and the one was likely to evoke the other.

Today one hears numerous discussions about who is or is not deviating from the true doctrine of psychoanalysis as promulgated by Freud. Often the ashes on Freud's altar are mistaken for the fire by those faithful followers whose dogmatic voices sound so strange in our era of modern science. Recently an orthodox psychoanalyst, in commenting on an address given by another psychoanalyst, said, "I do not know how one would classify his ideas on so-called analytic technique, but it is surely not psychoanalysis." His statement carried the reproachful ring of a Moses speaking to the children of Israel, "Put away that golden calf and turn back to the worship of the one true God."

Abse and Jessner, in discussing the psychodynamics of leadership, show how there remains in all of us from childhood a longing to find again, or to be, a godlike personage, unlimited in power and wisdom.[9] The authors go on to say that the follower's wish for a changed self-image, one of far greater strength, can be fulfilled only if the leader appears as an idealized alter ego, which then can become part of the follower. The leader, especially the charismatic leader, needs his followers as much as the actor needs his audience. In this interdependence he maintains the cohesion of the group to a considerable extent by keeping aggressiveness in suspense and by diverting it toward out-groups.[10] Thus, one who deviated within the group from the core beliefs of the other group members would naturally be expelled, or else the necessary cohesion of the group would be lost. In the development of Freudianism and Calvinism one can readily see the psychodynamics in operation as related to leader and follower.

Summary

Freud and Calvin were both great leaders who changed the course of history. Not only was their impact great upon the peoples of their own times but upon those of all subsequent times. These doctors, one of the mind, the other of the soul, were men of rare dimensions and rare contradictions.

Freud, before he went into medicine, wanted to be a lawyer as

[9] D. Wilfred Abse and Lucie Jessner, "The Psychodynamic Aspects of Leadership," *Daedalus*, Fall, 1961, pp. 693-710.

[10] *Ibid*; Joachim Flescher, "Political Life and Super-ego Regression," *Psychoanalytic Review*, XXXVI (1949), 416-28.

well as a politician or lawmaker. When, in 1938, he was exiled from his country by the Nazis, he carried with him a manuscript on Moses, the supreme lawgiver of the people, whose unique fate and gifts he had accepted as his own. Freud looked upon himself as another Moses who led man out of his captivity, gave him the knowledge to understand his nature, and helped him accept the laws which governed his nature.

Calvin, trained in both theology and the law, identified also with the role of lawmaker and lawgiver. His outlook on life was tinctured more with the spirit of Moses than with the spirit of Christ. He also sought to lead mankind out of bondage. He put together the solid foundation stones on which a sturdy moral structure could be reared.

III

RELIGION AND THE
EMOTIONALLY DISTURBED

6

The Use and Misuse of Religion
by the Emotionally Disturbed

It is often said that the way a person uses his religion is a good barometer of his mental health. My clinical observations have led me to believe that the positive, health-giving qualities of religion are too numerous to mention. Superficial observations by the psychiatrist may lead him to think that religion has been bad for his patient and that his patient has been the recipient of a "bad" religion. This may be true. Yet, more often, his patient has taken a basically healthy religious faith and distorted or modified it to serve the ends of his own psychological problems. If a psychiatrist's only concept of religion is acquired from mentally ill individuals, he could hardly be said to have a valid picture, or be expected to view religion with sympathy or understanding. This is probably what happened to Sigmund Freud, for his description of religion is distorted and highly biased. Harry Emerson Fosdick has commented that Freud's picture of religion is what should be more nearly described as sin.

Both the neurotic and the psychotic can distort doctrinal formulations. The psychotic's distortions are more bizarre and spectacular, attract attention, and are not infrequently cited by some students of human behavior in an attempt to reduce all religious experience to the level of psychological illness. Also, disturbed individuals can teach distorted and unhealthy interpretations to emotionally healthy people, especially children. Areas of conflict are created or, if already present, intensified.

The psychiatrist often sees long religious conflict as a cause or a contributing factor in the psychoses. He may also see religion as a precipitating factor in a psychotic break or used as a defense against a psychosis. Frequently he sees religion as a sup-

plier of the ideational form or content of the psychotic produc-
tions. The content of a patient's thoughts in psychotic illness is
often closely related to the previous character structure of the
patient. If religion concerns him prior to his illness, it is expected
that a religious coloring will enter his psychosis. It should be
stressed that if mental processes are disordered in psychoses,
should not one expect that a previously normal religious experience and orientation will be reacted to or expressed in a
disordered way in illness? The same holds for any other deep
concerns of patients, such as business, medicine, and science,
for the psychiatrist sees all these incorporated in the ideational
production of the psychotic. Yet popular misconception of this
has led to the belief among the laity that there is a specific mental illness known as "religious mania." And that the etiology of
this condition is generally overindulgence in religious practices.

Since we have learned much about the meaning of human
behavior from the disordered mind, we have also acquired a
broader understanding of religious needs and implications
through our work with the mentally ill.

The following is a discussion of the uses and misuses of religion by individuals in their adjustment problems of everyday
existence. It is of considerable interest to study some of these
distortions or modifications as they relate to doctrines of God,
man, sin, the church, healing, the Scriptures, Christian growth,
and symbolism. One must be careful, in such a study as this,
not to let the distortions seen in psychopathology devaluate or
stigmatize the normal in religious belief and experience.

Concept of God

Jesus illustrated his concept of God by relating the parable
of the prodigal son (Luke 15:11-32). This parable pictures God
as the loving and forgiving Father. Many people have no concept of a good father, for they have not had such a father. Thus
Jesus did not simply compare God with one's earthly father
but went a step further and showed what a good father is like
in words, attitudes, and actions. A child can understand Jesus'
picture of Divine goodness, estrangement from God, and resto-

ration. Many of our patients have parents far removed from the ideal picture described by Jesus, and in turn these same patients usually have a warped view of God.

If an individual looks upon God as punishing and judgmental, his life will be characterized by fear, ambivalences, and hidden resentments. Out of such a matrix an obsessive, compulsive neurosis often develops. Bigotry and fanaticism may also be a product of a belief in a harsh, judgmental God. The unforgiving legalist is another example of the individual whose concept of God is the very opposite of the loving Father. The heavy demands of a judgmental God and the unyielding boundaries of a relentless law give him narrow limits in which to operate and color all of his interpersonal relationships. In this type of psychopathology is often seen a confusion of the concept of God with the concept of self. The grandiosity of the perfectionist or unforgiving legalist is often created out of his need to be perfect, his need to be accepted by this harsh God who is satisfied with nothing less than perfection. It is easy for such a person to usurp the role of God. And the psychiatrist sees a number of such people both in and out of mental institutions.

Doctrine of Man

Man is a creature and is the crown of God's creation. He is neither beast nor angel; he is a human being. The psalmist sings, "Thou hast made him a little lower than the angels, and hast crowned him with glory and honor" (Ps. 8:5). In the book of Genesis is written, "God created man in his own image" (1:27).

When we contemplate the glorious origin and destiny of man, it is easy to lose our humility and become proud. When we compare our finiteness to God's infiniteness, we could be overwhelmed with feelings of weakness, inadequacy, and despair. Thus, man's conception of self has ranged from dust to God. Often one sees in certain individuals a compulsive necessity to carry out a certain plan, a definite mission. They may appropriate the messianic role. Actually, for the restless, hungering mind, it is easy to swing from the doctrine of *Vocatio Dei* to an exaggerated concept of one's call. In the patient's struggle to lift himself, to give a special meaning to his existence, he occasionally extends himself beyond the boundaries of realities.

A dramatic example of appropriating the messianic role is discussed in the chapter entitled "False Pregnancy in a Male."

Doctrine of Sin

It seems that sin is best defined as estrangement from God and not deviation from rules.

The psychiatric concept of the id, referring to the basic, unrefined biological impulses, does not differ to any great extent from that aspect of the theological doctrine of original sin, which refers to man's bondage to his primitive impulses, his rebellious nature, and his destructive tendencies.

Employment of a doctrine of sin by an individual or a group may range from condemnation—expressing self-hatred and hatred for the human race—to illuminating attempts to analyze and to understand the causes of human misery and bondage.

One occasionally sees a "hellfire and damnation" evangelist who breathes hatred with every sentence. From such a person we learn nothing about the love and forgiveness of God. Such a person is using a socially acceptable medium to express his own hate. He projects upon God his own attributes and makes God into his own image.

Some antivivisectionists are dealing with similar feelings. The unconscious motivation may be a contempt for their fellow human beings rather than a love of animals. When one of the Russian Sputniks carried a dog, some of the antivivisectionists wrote to the newspapers decrying the fact that a lovely animal was so sacrificed rather than one of the many worthless human beings who are always around. Thus the motivation here is not that they love animals so much but that they have a contempt for human beings.

Another aspect of this is the cruel aggressive tendencies in all of us, and our efforts to control them. When the antivivisectionist accuses the doctor of cruelty, he may be testifying that if he, himself, were dissecting laboratory animals it would be to gratify the cruel streak in his nature. Thus he projects his unconscious motivation onto the dissecting physician. If doctors are allowed to dissect, then he has less control over his unconscious hostile and cruel desires. He thus tries to stop the dissector in order to strengthen his own control.

Early in any psychotherapist's career he is confronted with patients grieving over having committed the unpardonable sin. This is an effective way of inflicting self-punishment. Proper elucidation of such a doctrine, or theological agreement as to its meaning, is hard to find. Patients generally interpret it as cursing God. Attendants in mental institutions often show profound anxiety when a patient begins to curse God. The attendants want to move out of the presence of such a patient as if fearing lightning to strike any moment in the area of the cursing.

The shadow of such a sin hung like a cloud over the life of Søren Kierkegaard. His father had been a poor boy who had attained a fortune as a merchant. He died in 1838, at more than eighty years of age. He was almost sixty when Søren was born. Before he died, he told his son the following story. He had worked as a shepherd in his youth. Once, while watching over his sheep in total loneliness, he cursed God. He was never able to rid himself of this sin. He was a sober and somewhat melancholy man. He could never enjoy himself. One can only speculate as to how much this curse motivated his unhappiness, or how much the curse was motivated by an unfortunate personality makeup. The sensitive, devout Søren was immensely impressed with his father's confession and was perhaps unable ever to rid himself entirely of its impact. The following statement of his sheds light on this speculation: "Scripture teaches that God visits the sin of the fathers upon the children unto the third and fourth generation; verily, life is telling this in a loud voice."

An important aspect of the religious life is confession of one's sins and acknowledgment of defects. This may range from extreme pessimism and crystalized immaturity to a sound safeguard against illusions of self-sufficiency, delusions of grandeur, and self-righteousness.

In any discussion of sin one is confronted with the necessity of mentioning normal and neurotic guilt. Normal guilt follows in the wake of wrongdoing, seen and accepted as such by the doer. He seeks expiation and makes restitution. It is a conscious phenomenon, involving deeds we have done. Neurotic or pathological guilt has its roots deep in the unconscious mind, and the individual cannot rid himself of this by the usual methods of atonement. In pathological guilt, the intent, even unconscious, is equated with the deed, and the person reacts to the unconscious intent as if it were an already accomplished misdeed. Often the obsessive, compulsive neurotic unconsciously considers wrong what he unconsciously wishes to do. Thus his endless rituals and gyrations to atone are understandable. They are endless because relief seems never to come. The depressed person may be dealing with unconscious wishes as if they were already committed acts.

A forty-year-old woman—a devout and faithful member of the Roman Catholic Church—came for psychiatric treatment when encouraged to do so by her family physician and her priest. She had suffered from feelings of guilt from which she never received complete relief in the confessional. She had many eccentricities which annoyed and inconvenienced the family, such as never letting any relatives baby-sit with her children. In the process of treatment it was discovered that when she was about six years of age her sister and brother-in-law stayed with her some evenings as baby-sitters. When she was in bed, her brother-in-law would visit her bedroom and stroke the inside of her thighs. She had felt that he forced her to submit to this, but in treatment she discovered that she had encouraged him. The discussion of this incident was a genuine cathartic experience, upsetting her to such an extent that she remained in bed several days after the abreaction. She was then freed of this pathological guilt and felt at peace with herself for the first time in her memory. Much of her guilt stemmed from aspects of the situation which she had repressed but not well enough to give her comfort. Thus, there poured from her unconscious mind these festering guilty fears which influenced her behavior in many areas of her personal and family life.

Mission and Role of the Church

Any statement regarding the church's role, made by a psychiatrist (even one with theological training), can only cover a few aspects of this broad subject. It is generally conceded that the church seeks through its fellowship to bring salvation to the world and to demonstrate a way of life which is valid for the needs of men and nations. As man relates himself to the church in work and worship, there develops the uneasy equilibrium of his impact upon the church and the church's impact upon him. He may look upon this covenant community as a sanctuary for saints or a hospital for sinners. He may regard all economic, political, and social problems as falling outside of the church's task of soul-saving, or at least, relatively unimportant even in the total ministry of the church. Yet he may stress social salvation as an important part of the church's mission, and proposals of social reform may range from unrealistic idealism to a practical implementation of democracy; from ill-advised alliances between the church and social movements to prophetic protest and revolutionary action.

Conceptions of the purity of the church may range in a man's mind from self-righteous separation from the world to complete solidarity with other men in compassion and self-giving.

He may interpret the doctrinal formulations of the church as rigid, lifeless systems or as vital, symbolic expressions of human experience and divine revelation. One has only to listen to a few severe neurotics or schizophrenics with religious concern to find a patient who can squeeze out of any tenet of faith its healing power.

The ability of the stable or unstable mind to appropriate the resources of the church varies widely. One's ability to utilize the church's healing forces in calm or in crisis is one of the greatest prophylactics in maintaining mental health.

Ministry of Healing

The church has an important part to play in divine healing. Probably no other area of the church's ministry has attracted more disturbed people, falling in diagnostic categories from psychopath to paranoid schizophrenic. Many have good intentions; others exploit what they are doing with conscious awareness. As there are multiple factors which may contribute to the precipitation of an illness, so there are multiple factors which enter into the restoration of health. Religious ministration may have a profound bearing upon the emotional and spiritual life of the patient and may be the necessary ingredient for recovery. Theologians and psychiatrists ought to continue to examine critically but sympathetically the phenomenon of faith healing.

There is a tendency of some clergymen to stress a dichotomy between "spiritual healing" and "scientific healing." This leads to the temptation to make faith a substitute for medical skill or to depreciate the work of physicians. Especially is this temptation great when emotional disorders are dealt with. The physician is hesitant to claim any ability to heal. His efforts have been in the direction of removing the obstacles which interfere with healing or creating a more favorable environment for healing. A French surgeon of the sixteenth century, Ambroise Paré, expressed this concept in memorable words for all physicians of all times: "God heals the wound; I merely dress it." This is his testimony that all healing comes from God.

Thus the surgeon, in the care of the wound, cleanses it, removes the debris, and brings together the edges of the skin. All he can do is remove the obstacles to healing, and this he does. He is not the source of healing and knows little about the nature of healing—only the obstacles to healing. Even in psychotherapy we are only removing the psychological obstacles to healing, but the healing itself comes from God, regardless of by what name he is called. Although the cleansing and dressing of a psychological wound is a more complicated technique, requiring value judgments not needed by the surgeon, the recognition of God as the source of all healing will help us keep our efforts in the proper perspective, regardless of the professional disciplines we represent.

Protestantism's doctrine of the priesthood of all believers puts the Christian physician in a very special place in the healing ministry. God can communicate through the physician's medical knowledge and also act directly as person-to-person through his Christian dedication. This is emphasized because certain clergymen have a tendency to place healing which takes place through the assistance of the clergyman as superior to that which occurs through the efforts of the physician. The physician is aware of the great role of the church in sacramental healing, that is, healing mediated through the church and its sacraments and rites. He is also aware of the charismatic healer who seems to be endowed with intrinsic powers of healing.

Doctrine of the Scriptures

The Bible is a spiritual book and not a book of science. It is not a source for bibliolatry. It contains the story of God's progressive revelation of himself to man. In conveying its teachings and concepts various techniques of language are used. The interpretive battle of literalistic versus figurative language has raged through the centuries. Men have gone to extremes on both sides and their concerns have found expression in both their health and illness.

Many of the scriptural exhortations are capable of enslaving a person or giving the freedom for Christian growth. The following passages are taken as examples, for they are often quoted by patients:

"Know ye not that your body is the temple of the Holy Ghost?" (I Cor. 5:19.) This statement may lead to a wholesome concept of body physiology, or on the other hand, to marked inhibitions, repression, and denial of all biological impulses—leading to sexual crippling and the viewing of bodily functions as dirty. Those who stress the dichotomy of spirit versus flesh are generally those who consider everything physical as unclean and evil. This often represents a major effort on their part to control their strong, overwhelming id impulses—their way of keeping the "lid on the id." They utilize freely such mechanisms as denial, projection, suppression, and repression.

"Be ye therefore perfect, even as your Father which is in

heaven is perfect." (Matt. 5:48.) This is interpreted by the well-balanced Christian as a striving toward a high and lofty goal, with the full realization that such a goal is unattainable. A distortion of this doctrine leads to obsessive, perfectionistic behavior, the unforgiving legalist, the hypercritical person who requires the impossible of himself and those around him.

"And if thy right hand offend thee, cut it off, and cast it from thee: for it is profitable for thee that one of thy members should perish, and not that thy whole body should be cast into hell." (Matt. 5:30.) A literal interpretation of this passage would lead to an extreme in behavior for most of us, for on some levels we have offended ourselves with some part or organ of the body. There are those who have acted upon this exhortation. I saw a woman in a mental institution who had disarticulated her right hand at the wrist and thrown the hand away. She sat quietly all day with the open Bible resting on the stump—even when she was doing odd tasks with the other hand, such as folding clothes. In the same institution there was a girl who had to be restrained most of the time to prevent her from plucking out her eyes, in an effort to abide by this same scriptural passage.

"But the end of all things is at hand: be ye therefore sober, and watch unto prayer." (I Pet. 4:7.) It is a commonly accepted belief among biblical scholars that Jesus felt the end of the world was imminent. This belief was shared by the early Christians, and their thoughts and actions were guided by this eschatological viewpoint. Various groups through the centuries have predicted the end of the world at a particular moment in history and prepared themselves by selling their property and putting all earthly matters in order. Many mental patients have eschatological concerns. They believe the world has, is, or will come to an end. Some ask to be buried, stating that they are already dead and want to prepare for the resurrection.

The efforts to make out of the Bible a book of science have clouded the understanding of both the ordered and the disordered mind. Countless passages of scripture could be cited as furnishing the material for this endeavor—chief among them, the first few chapters of the book of Genesis.

The Bible is often used as an amulet. One schizophrenic slept with the Bible and a sharp ax under his bed to "cut" the evil spirits which bothered him at night. A man with a toxic psychosis following heavy intake of wine heard a male and a female voice threatening him. He found temporary relief by reading the Bible. When he came to a "powerful" verse while reading, the voices would flee to save themselves from destruction. He could not predict what verses would be successful. He had to read at random until he found a potent verse. He had better luck with the book of Psalms than with other books. Also, he slept with the Bible under his pillow and this kept the voices away. However, they would come and, upon discovering the Bible, would make only one comment each. The male voice would say, "We ought to kill the worthless bastard." The female voice would reply, "We better not with the Bible under his pillow, for we might get killed." We found tranquilizer drugs a good competitor with the Bible in controlling his auditory hallucinations. Shortly after being put on drugs he heard only one voice, "Drink Thunderbird." This continued in a repetitive pattern for about twenty-four hours and then ceased.

"I must work the works of him that sent me, while it is day: the night cometh, when no man can work." (John 9:4.) This is a strong plea to be diligent as a laborer in God's vineyard. One's attitude toward duty can range from compulsive legalism to an ethical outlook which provides for creative cooperation between conscience and instinctual impulses. Many guilt-ridden individuals often exhaust themselves in the "vineyard" in efforts to atone through almost self-punishing toil.

Doctrine of Christian Growth

Dependence upon God and the Christian church can range from infantile escapism to a healthy acceptance of human limitations and finiteness.

One readily sees among church members a wide spectrum of emotional development, ranging from coercive dependence to a healthy blend of dependence and independence. The lady who calls her minister or other church officials several times every day to get reassurance that she is or will be "saved" is surely a narcissistic, coercive, dependent person. Children of possessive, overindulgent parents are often the victims of a dependency relationship which interferes severely with growth away from the mother to health and independence. In all early religio-social cultures where the Earth Mother was the goddess venerated, the greatest withdrawal of her favor was from the regressive worshiper. Primitive man was well aware of the fact that the individual who is not allowed or not able to sacrifice his dependence upon comfort and security will not, in later life, have the capacity to make those psychic sacrifices which alone can help him to mature in his relationship with God and his fellow man. These are the ones who lose faith in God in the face of hardships or of unanswered prayer. They are the ones who use the church as a big breast for them alone to suckle upon and get upset if they catch others suckling at a time when they want to suck.

A conversion experience ought to be examined and not taken for granted, for it can represent regression or maturation. Conversion may represent a turning back to childhood values or an acceptance of a new and mature set of values.

Symbolism

The church uses many symbols. Its members often speak or write in symbolic language. Its hymns proclaim, "Lord, speak to me." The dove is the symbol of the Holy Spirit. The lamb, the shepherd, the cross, are fraught with symbolic meaning.

A Roman Catholic priest referred to me a patient who had moved from the Baptist to the Episcopal to the Roman Catholic Church. The priest mentioned that he had seen a number of schizophrenic individuals who, in their mental illnesses, had moved rather rapidly from one church to another—and almost invariably had moved from a less ritualistic church with a few symbols to a more ritualistic or liturgical one with many symbols.

This type of religious behavior represents a dramatic struggle to stave off disintegration and bring to pass healing. The patient described made a reparative effort in this direction when he joined the Episcopal Church, but a more definitive effort as he moved on to Roman Catholicism.

It is interesting that religious symbolism was caught up in this patient's efforts to find health. Part of the evaluation of every mental patient is to check his language for abstract and concrete thinking, for the way he is using symbols.

The severe mental patient often takes excessive liberties with man's gift of symbolization. The ability to assign a symbol to an object, idea, or value permits communication across ages and among people. The schizophrenic illness is often best characterized by overly general abstractions that violate socially accepted rules of logic. Thus, both the literal and figurative properties of religious teachings become even more symbolically abstract, encompassing meanings that escape validation. A patient's autistic religious symbolization, representing the most florid symptoms of his illness, can be handled or checked somewhat by the patient's movement from a religion that permits more independent symbol interpretation to one with increased dogma and definition, where the abstractions and their limits are clearly restricted for the individual.

Conclusion

Clinical concepts, which refer to reason and order, lose some of their significance when we enter the life of the spirit. Distinctions between what is healthy and what is morbid in the spiritual life are not always obvious to the clinician. The early Christians were often confused by the claims and behavior of some of their followers. They adopted a rule by which to evaluate, which has validity to this day: "By their fruits ye shall know them" (Matt. 7:20).

The study of our patients reveals how varied is the expression of religious experience and ideas. If the psychiatrist is presented with an individual who expresses the content of his thoughts in religious terms, he must be able to come to a conclusion about the patient's mental condition. It is never the religious expression as such that leads to the diagnosis of mental illness, but an assessment of the total situation within which that expression arises. This evaluation is based upon well-established diagnostic criteria. The important fact for all to be aware of, especially the pastoral counselor, is that mental illness may present a predominantly religious symptomatology. This recognition may save the individual from unnecessary delays in the institution of treatment.

7
Suicide:
Its Meaning and Prevention

Suicide is the ninth leading cause of death in the United States, and probably deserves a level much higher than ninth in mortality statistics. It is estimated that there are over 500,000 suicide attempts a year in this country, with death resulting from less than 5 per cent of them, or about 18,000 to 20,000.

The incidence is actually much higher than that given here. A substantial number of deaths due to suicide are not so recorded on death certificates because of religious, social, moral, or other forms of stigma. In this respect suicide shares the dubious honor of secrecy with alcoholism, drug addiction, mental illness, and venereal disease. Many deaths of adults due to the ingestion of toxic substances, particularly when large numbers of barbiturate capsules are taken alone or in combination with alcohol, are classified as accidental when in reality they are intentional. Many deaths due to gas poisoning, whether in the garage, over the kitchen range, or in the bathroom, similarly are listed as accidental when they, too, should fall in the intentional group. To these one can add many more—the slow suicide of chronic alcoholism, the ruthless suicide of far too many automobile accidents, and, increasingly, the subtle suicide of overdosing with tranquilizers. Together these would raise the total to the much more realistic figure of possibly 50,000 to 60,000 cases per year.

The problem is a complex one, with no single factor which can be assumed as *the* cause. Even when one has extensive records on a suicide case, which he has studied thoroughly, there remain baffling facets and unanswered questions. Heraclitus' words, written centuries ago, are applicable but not especially comforting as one tries to understand this phenomenon. "You cannot find the boundaries of the soul, even if you travel every road; so deep is the measure of it." However, the nature and degree of the internal stress and the external evidence of it can be searched for and found.

Thus, it is important to search our clinical records for new clues to understanding this kind of human behavior, for new ways to detect the potential candidate and, when detected, to help him find a healthier solution to his problems. Epidemiological studies are indicated as well as other public health measures. Suicide is a preventable phenomenon and thus should challenge every worker in the field of medical and social sciences, as well as that of religion.

To the average person in this country suicide seems too dreadful and senseless to be conceivable. There actually seems to be a kind of taboo on the serious discussion of it. There has never been a national campaign against it such as there has been against other, less easily preventable forms of death. Some organized public interest is beginning to develop in the area of prevention, and some scientific research concerning it is now being carried out. There seems to be a trend currently that may well be a reflection of a growing psychological orientation in American culture to view some activities, such as the behavior of persons under psychological duress, as public health responsibilities, and to seek to understand the motivations underlying these behaviors within the milieu in which they occur. Yet any student of this complex psychologic, psychiatric, and sociologic phenomenon cannot help being surprised at how little investigation and analysis has been accorded suicide.

Society's attitudes and feelings toward self-destruction have been manifested with considerable variability from early recorded history to the present—ranging from severe condemnation to acceptance and incorporation into a way of life, as in the Japanese samurai code of hara-kiri and the Indian custom of suttee. In spite of variations, the predominant attitude of civilized society toward suicide today is one of condemnation.

Motivation in Suicide

The best-known theoretical framework for understanding the psychodynamics of suicide is that elucidated by Karl Menninger.[1] Three components comprise this theory, and all three are present in varying degrees in each suicidal act. The three components are: (1) the wish to kill (conscious hate); (2) the wish to be killed (conscious guilt feelings); (3) the wish to die (conscious hopelessness, worthlessness, and despair). Menninger's theory, however, owes much to Freud's view expressed in the paper "Mourning and Melancholia," which describes the dynamics of depression as essentially the turning of an individual's sadism against himself.[2] Although Freud's paper dealt with the dynamics of depression, it also provided the basis for the psychoanalytic theory of suicide. Basic to this theory is the concept that aggression becomes turned upon the self when an object that is both loved and hated is lost. In Freud's words, "No neurotic harbours thoughts of suicide which are not murderous impulses against others re-directed upon himself."

Otto Fenichel extends Freud's basic theory and states that suicide is the result of a strong ambivalent (submissive fear and coercive rage) dependence on a cruel conscience and the necessity to get rid of the unbearable tension of strong guilt feelings.[3] He goes on to say that to have a desire to live evidently means to feel a certain self-esteem, and to feel supported by the protective forces of the conscience. When this feeling vanishes, the original feeling of annihilation experienced by the deserted hungry infant reappears. Since the conscience is composed of introjects which represent incorporated love objects, suicide represents an extreme form of submission to the cruel conscience on one hand, and on the other hand involves the murder of the original object or objects whose incorporation helped to

[1] *Man Against Himself* (New York: Harcourt, Brace, 1938), pp. 24-81.
[2] *Collected Papers*, ed. E. Jones, tr. J. Riviere (London: Hogarth Press, 1953), IV, 152-70.
[3] *The Psychoanalytic Theory of Neurosis* (New York: W. W. Norton & Company, 1945), pp. 399-401.

create the conscience.[4] This is murder of the kind of Dorian Gray's murder of his image.

No psychiatrist has been more articulate or clearer in elucidating the dynamic pattern in depression than Sander Rado.[5] He pictures the depressive spell as a desperate cry for love, precipitated by an actual or imagined loss, which the patient feels endangers his emotional and material security. The patient has lost his loved one. The emotional overreaction to this emergency unfolds, without the patient's awareness, as an expiatory process of self-punishment. Through blaming and punishing himself for the loss he has suffered, he hopes to reconcile the "mother" and to reinstate himself into her loving care. His dominant motivation of repentance, however, is complicated by the simultaneous presence of an intense resentment. His guilty fears push him toward humility and repentance; his coercive rage pushes him toward resentfulness. In the forephase of the depressive spell the patient has a tendency to pour out his resentment on the beloved person—the one who deserted him or let him down. This is an effort to force the person to love him. When the patient feels that his coercive rage has been defeated, his need for repentance becomes dominant. His rage then recoils and turns inward against himself, increasing by its fervor the severity of his self-reproaches and self-punishment. As a supreme maneuver for forgiveness, the patient may be driven to suicide. As he attempts to end his life, he seems to be acting under the illusion that his supreme sacrifice will reconcile the loved one and secure her nourishing graces—forever.

Durkheim used a sociologic approach in his monumental

[4] As regarding introjects in conscience formation, Fenichel is referring to the development of conscience in the child through incorporating within himself moral standards, his parents, heroes about which he reads, important figures in his community such as his teachers, his minister, and so on. These incorporated figures are all called *imagoes*, and they become a part of his inner self. Suicide then could be directed against these internalized figures which went into the formation of the person's conscience.

[5] *Psychoanalysis of Behavior* (New York: Grune & Stratton, 1956), pp. 236-40.

study of suicide.[6] His book, first published in 1897, is looked upon by many as an outstanding, if not the most outstanding, work on social causation. What he sought to establish was that a seemingly individual and very personal phenomenon can be adequately explained by examining the social structure and its various functions. In essence, Durkheim's theory proposes that the social structure determines in large measure the degree to which an individual is "integrated" into his society. Suicide can then result when this integration is not at an appropriate level. Three types of suicide are described.

The first is *egoistic suicide,* in which the individual is inadequately integrated into his society. A good example is the situation of the aged in America today. Even though these people have the same orientation toward societal values as in their earlier years, such as productivity and accomplishment, our society's identification with them has diminished. Because of such factors as forced retirement and the "glorification of youth," older people today occupy a lower status position than before, and this gives rise to feelings of rejection and loneliness—and a consequently higher suicide rate.

Second, there is *altruistic suicide,* in which there is an over-integration of the individual with society. The individual's life is rigorously governed by custom and habit, and he may commit suicide through obedience to higher commands, such as those of religious sacrifice, or through blind political allegiance. The Kamikazi pilots of World War II would fit this category.

The third type is *anomic suicide,* in which there is a lack of regulation of the individual by society. Such events as economic depression or sudden wealth can disrupt societal adjustment, and the former rules of conduct become inapplicable to the new situation.

Durkheim felt that there was an antithesis between the social and individual psychopathological explanations of suicide. Actually they are complementary. Modern methods of psycho-

---

[6] Émile Durkheim, *Suicide: A Study in Sociology,* tr. and ed. by J. A. Spaulding and G. Simpson (Glencoe, Ill.: Free Press, 1950), pp. 14-15.

analysis were unknown to Durkheim. Freud had just begun his investigations of the unconscious determinants of human behavior when Durkheim's sociologic study of suicide appeared. The task which lies ahead is to interrelate the life histories of individual suicides with sociological variables, on the hypothesis that certain subcultures or social environments may induce, perpetuate, or aggravate the suicide potential. In this way we may be in a position to establish generalized occurrence.[7]

Eissler holds the thesis that suicide is the result of rebellion against death.[8] He feels that for most people the idea of having to die is unbearable. In committing suicide one believes he has cheated death, as the condemned man cheats the executioner and the waiting crowd when he kills himself. He goes on to say that probably for most suicides the act does not mean really dying, since dying is something which is passively submitted to. When actively carried out, it becomes a triumph, as if the ego has proved itself to be almighty by being strong enough to cast its own life aside.

Because of the danger and unpredictability of the suicide attempt, it has been likened to gambling and the urge to challenge fate. "Psychopathologically, both seem to spring from the urge to test the balance between the libidinal and life-preserving tendencies on the one hand and the destructive impulses on the other."[9]

Many cases of suicide are caused by the feeling that life has been a failure and that it is not worth living any more. One then commits suicide, just as a businessman declares bankruptcy when losses exceed gains and there is no more hope for recovering the losses.

The following notes, left by two patients of mine, seem to

[7] Durkheim's pupil, M. Halbwachs, extended the work of his teacher by advocating the combination of sociological with psychological and clinical approaches as a better method of providing some answers to the problem of suicide. See M. Halbwachs, Les Causes du Suicide (Paris, 1930).

[8] Kurt R. Eissler, The Psychiatrist and the Dying Patient (New York: International Universities Press, 1955), p. 66.

[9] E. Stengel and N. G. Cook, Attempted Suicide: Its Social Significance and Effects (London: Chapman and Hall, 1958), p. 118.

illustrate well the view just presented. Both of these patients survived, although they made serious attempts and came close to death. The first note was written by an intelligent twenty-three-year-old girl, married to a graduate student. The second one was written by a twenty-eight-year-old woman, married to a promising young artist. Each note is addressed to the husband.

Please forgive me, but I can't stand myself any longer. I'm just a weakling. Please, please forgive me. I've asked the Lord to forgive me, too. He will, for He is good and understands.

No one is to blame but myself. I just couldn't accept my limitations. Now I know I couldn't be a good wife to anyone. I'm too weak —too stupid. I don't want to be a drag on anyone any longer. My [husband's name] is wonderful. I could never love anyone but you, but all I've done to you (and Mother, too) is cause you heartache. I've tried to hold on to you, but it isn't fair to you. Love [Name].

I know you want to be a painter dear—at the cost of all else—so Godspeed to you—and take care of the girls—[daughter's name] has it in her to be a good painter—but tonight she told me she wanted to be a nurse—encourage her in whichever direction she wants to go— you can do it much better than I—don't blame yourself—above all don't blame yourself—I would just hang on to you—I know why you went to the party tonite—so I'm going to die—very shortly—because no one cares—thank you for giving me the opportunity—not nasty— and I don't think I'm being selfish—I just don't want the girls to turn out as I did—help them and for God's sake help yourself, now, while you've got time—is there anything else—only that I loved you in the wrong way but I did love you. I haven't made any blames on you altho' I've felt some—it's all been a chain reaction—only I didn't realize how I'd hurt you—we were wrong—there's a lot more but I haven't time—tell the girls that I may not have been much of a mother but I did love them—I tried to tell [daughter's name] to-nite—I love you my dearest but to have three children on your hands is a little too much—I love you—[Name].

Suicide in the geriatric age group merits a separate discussion. Suicide is not uncommon in elderly people. Depressive illness is prevalent in the older age group and one could list multiple etiological factors—among them death of loved ones, declining physical health, change in work status (retirement, loss of job), and mental deterioration. Confusional states following surgical procedures, severe physical illness, or other forms of stress sometimes lead to suicide if the patient is not protected during this period. The confusional state is characterized by the clouding of consciousness and disorientation. Its onset is sudden and its duration is short. In old age the majority of suicidal people are psychotic or close to a psychosis. They can be included generally in two clinical groups: the depressive states, and the chronic brain syndromes due to cerebral arteriosclerosis or senility. The best-known prophylactic measures against mental breakdowns in elderly people are to see that they are socially integrated in the community and that they feel useful, valued, accepted, and loved. Although vitamin deficiency may be a problem with some elderly people, more of them suffer from *purpose deficiency* and *people deficiency*.

As for suicide in children, including adolescents, there are also multiple motivations. However, the major psychodynamic factor is the real or threatened loss of a love object. Deprivation of love is an unbearable situation for some children.[10] When a child feels the threat of the loss of a love object, he develops feelings of rage toward the frustrating object, plus feelings of worthlessness and helplessness. Clinically, he then appears depressed. The mechanism is not too different from that of depression in adults. The rage against the frustrating parent is turned inward, but the suicidal child goes a step further and makes a desperate attempt at regaining contact with the lost love object. Thus the suicide act represents a type of restitutional phenomenon.[11] The child, through suicide or other self-destructive acts, attacks the internalized love object and through the attack attempts to recover it. This is similar to the belief

[10] L. Bender and P. Schilder, "Suicidal Preoccupations and Attempts in Children," *American Journal of Orthopsychiatry*, VII (1937), 225-34.
[11] G. Rochlin, "Loss and Restitution," in *Psychoanalytic Study of the Child* (New York: International Universities Press, 1953), VIII, 288-309.

that through death one is united with the love object. Such a belief is dramatized in Shakespeare's *Romeo and Juliet*.

Also the child often wishes to punish the depriving, frustrating figure by the induction of guilt.[12] This is illustrated in Mark Twain's *Tom Sawyer*. Tom was frustrated by his aunt, and he was comforted by the fantasy of committing suicide by drowning himself in the Mississippi. He thought to himself how remorseful his aunt would be when his pale, limp body would be brought into her presence. He imagined her saying: "Oh, if I had only loved him more. How differently I would have treated him if I had only known." The progression can be seen more easily if the steps are put in tabular form:

1. The real or threatened loss of a love object.
2. The child develops rage toward the frustrating love object.
3. Feelings of guilt arise, and then the rage is turned upon self.
4. Feelings of worthlessness and helplessness appear.
5. A desperate effort to regain contact with the lost, gratifying love object.
6. The suicide act represents a type of restitutional phenomenon.
7. A wish to punish the depriving figure by induction of guilt.
8. Children's suicide notes often imply that they still expect to be around.

The act of suicide seems even more puzzling if one believes, with Silverberg,[13] that the ego's main purpose and motive is to insure survival, and that this drive does not require a rational basis. I interviewed hundreds of Allied prisoners as they were being released from Japanese prison camps after World War II. They had lived in the most miserable of circumstances, in the midst of starvation, death, disease, and abuse—yet they clung

[12] This mechanism is used also by adults. Literature furnishes an excellent clinical illustration. Anna Karenina, before throwing herself beneath the wheels of a passing train, contemplated the guilt her suicide would induce in her husband Vronsky: "To die! And he will feel remorse; will love me; he will suffer on my account." Leo Tolstoy, *Anna Karenina*, tr. C. Garnett (Garden City, N.Y.: International Collectors Library, 1954), p. 672.

[13] W. V. Silverberg, *Childhood Experience and Personal Destiny* (New York: Springer Publishing Co., 1952), pp. 25-26.

tenaciously to life. No matter how desperate the circumstances are to which we may be reduced, most of us still wish to live and are loathe to end our lives. This is eloquently described by the old woman in Voltaire's *Candide:* [14]

I have grown old in misery and shame, with only half a backside; a hundred times I wanted to kill myself but I still loved life. This ridiculous weakness is perhaps the most disastrous of our inclinations; for is there anything sillier than to desire to bear continually a burden one always wishes to throw on the ground; to look upon oneself with horror and yet to cling to oneself; in short, to caress the serpent which devours us until he has eaten our heart?

Freud concluded that basically there are only two sources of instinctual energy in man—Eros and Thanatos, life and death. His concept of the "death instinct" has been both misunderstood and neglected. The essence of the theory seems to show that the organism strives *to safeguard its own individual path toward death.* Thus the organism defends itself against the dangers which would allow it to reach the end through a shortcut. As psychiatrist Gotthard Booth has pointed out, although Freud considered this behavior as evidence of the power of instinct over the intellect, he lived up to his insight through sixteen years of fighting off his cancer of the jaw, working in self-fulfillment to his last day.

Suicide may seem to contradict the primacy of the drive for survival. This is true only if suicide is taken at its face value. Suicide for many is an act of vengeance and murder, often cal-

[14] Just as eloquent a testimony can be drawn from real life to show the courage and dignity man can summon from within himself when the only logical course seems to be to lie down and die. Recently I met a beautiful woman of Jewish extraction who had spent World War II in Nazi concentration camps. She was put in prison when she was seventeen. Her mother and three siblings died while imprisoned. She developed tuberculosis but managed to survive. She stated that nobody expected to survive the imprisonment. In one year in her barracks building, only forty-seven out of two hundred were left. They died of typhus, tuberculosis, starvation, and other causes. She saw only one person commit suicide. They clung to life even when hope was gone. There was high voltage barbed wire around the camps, and to die one had only to touch the wire. Yet only one did.

culated to torture. Also the act of suicide seems postulated upon a conviction of survival in some form. As mentioned earlier, many suicide notes seem to imply that the victim still plans to be around.

If one deciphers carefully the theories of motivation, the causes for successful suicides or suicidal attempts can be partially grouped into these categories:

1. Anger which is internalized or retroflexed and manifests itself in the form of guilt and depression.

2. Attempts to manipulate another, to gain love and affection, or to punish another.

3. A signal of distress—a cry for help addressed to a significant person or persons in the social environment.

4. Reactions to feelings of internal disintegration, as a response to hallucinatory commands or delusional ideation.

5. A desire to join a dead relative or loved one may be the all-consuming drive.

6. Longing for sleep or surcease from pain—Nirvana.

7. Wish to be born again blamelessly.

8. Running away from an intolerable situation.

9. To wipe the slate clean, to turn defeat into victory—thus an act of atonement, purification, and honor—as in the Japanese culture.

10. The search for closure, such as an elderly person longing for death as a well-deserved closure to a rich and full life.

11. The longing for a spiritual rebirth.

12. The final category simply points to a question asked not infrequently: Does the human being have values that transcend his own survival, and are there situations when a person, in order to fulfill his existence, needs to bring his life to a close?

The Statistical Picture

A discussion of certain aspects of statistical patterns in general seems indicated at this point.

There is a distinct difference in the suicide pattern of the two sexes. All studies indicate that more men than women commit suicide; the ratio is generally three or four to one for the United States. Of considerable interest, however, is the fact that women account for more of the attempted suicides. A partial explanation of this pattern is in the method employed by the two sexes. Men choose the more violent and sudden means of self destruction, such as firearms and hanging, whereas women are more prone to methods which allow time for rescue, such as drugs and gas.

The suicide incidence increases with age, but this holds only up to a point for women. To the age of 50 or 60, the pattern is similar for both sexes, but from this point on the female incidence of suicide begins to level off and after 70 even declines slightly, while the male rate steadily climbs without any leveling off. This is probably true because women are less affected by the change in work status and resulting mental disturbance that old age entails. Males over 70 in the United States have an annual incidence rate of about 45 per 100,000.

Two or three times as many whites commit suicide as do Negroes in the United States.

The relationship of suicide and mental illness has posed particular difficulties for students of the problem. Many anthropological studies of primitive cultures place suicide in a context apparently different from mental disease. The act is understood by primitives chiefly in demonological, magical, or theological terms, with external powers considered to be playing a role in causation. According to anthropologists, committing suicide as a response to a shameful setback, or as an expression of hostility and spite, is a "normal" reaction. Analysis of data contained in the records of police departments suggest that about 20 per cent of suicides in the United States suffered from a major mental disorder.

Central to Durkheim's theory of suicide is the concept that the relational system of an individual confers security and stability, and that in any society where this system is weakened, the suicide incidence should rise. This idea is accepted today in almost unaltered form and is used to explain many of the variations in the suicide pattern. For instance:

1. The suicide rate for the married is lower than that for the single, widowed, or divorced. It is highest for the divorced, and

higher for widowed individuals than single ones up to the age of 35, at which time the relationship is reversed.[15] The family, then, is able to give security to the person.

2. Proportionately there are more suicides in the city than in the country. Urban life results in anonymity and freedom from controls—the controls on which the integrity of the relational system depends.

3. In certain populations suicides are highest in the high and low occupational status groups and lowest in the middle. It is not that wealth or poverty predispose a person to suicide, but that motility in social class and occupation leads to a lack of cohesion. Studies show that many suicides are "recent arrivals" in their social position, be it high or low, and have not yet gained stable orientation (Durkheim's "anomic suicide").

4. Religion is thought to be a preventative against suicide depending on how formal and binding the particular teachings are. Indeed, the data show that the order of incidence from high to low is Protestant, Roman Catholic, and Jewish. It cannot be all this simple, however, for while many Roman Catholic countries have a low rate, Spain's has tripled in the last fifty years.

The World Health Organization gathers from many countries mortality statistics from suicide. If one studies these statistics, available from thirty-four countries during the past ten years, he finds the highest rates for both sexes from West Berlin, East Germany, Hungary, Austria, Finland, Switzerland, Japan, Denmark, and Sweden. The lowest rates are found in Italy, Spain, Ireland, North Ireland, the nonwhite population of the United States, Colombia, and Costa Rica.

The annual suicide mortality rates per 100,000 range from 34 for West Berlin to 2.5 for Ireland.

In all the countries where statistics are available the female rate is lower than the male for all ages taken together and, also, with a few exceptions, for each of the individual age groups. The male-female ratio varies widely, from more than 4 to 1 in Portu-

---

[15] J. Hirsch, "Demography of Suicide," *Mental Hygiene*, XLIII (1959), 516-25.

gal to only 1.5 to 1 in Japan. The exceptions to masculine predominance are of some interest, as they all relate to the 15 through 19 age group. Within this group the female suicide rate has exceeded the male in Venezuela, Ceylon, Israel, West Berlin, Italy, and Portugal on a number of occasions during the past decade.

It is interesting to note that many of the countries which are democratic, peaceful, and prosperous have not only the highest suicide but also the highest alcoholism rates. These findings raise the question as to whether there is not something fundamentally wrong with our way of life and with the goals toward which we are striving. Sometimes, our life of prosperity is able to satisfy only our material needs but leaves us bored and spiritually empty. Suicide and alcoholism then become ways of escape. These findings illustrate dramatically the ancient wisdom that "man cannot live by bread alone."

The Cry for Help

As has been previously discussed, the act of suicide often seems postulated upon a conviction of survival in some form. Thus, suicide may not always contradict the primacy of the drive for survival. This issue becomes clearer if self-destructive tendencies are not regarded as the only motivating force in suicide attempts. In discussing suicide one should think in terms of two groups: (1) those who attempt suicide and survive; and (2) those who are successful in killing themselves. The suicide attempt seems to be a desperate cry for help. The person may or may not be consciously aware of his appeal to the human environment for some kind of rescue. Although a suicide attempt has an appeal function, this does not necessarily make it a hysterical gesture. Suicide attempts frequently occur in hysterics, because hysterics avail themselves of, and accentuate, common behavior patterns, preferably those of high communicative value. Thus it seems unwise to use the term "hysterical gesture" in describing any suicide attempt.

Research in the last few years on suicide and suicidal attempts

112

has emphasized that the intent to commit suicide is frequently and repeatedly communicated. In reviewing the records of seventy-five consecutive patients whom I saw while a resident psychiatrist at Charity Hospital in New Orleans, and who had made suicide gestures or attempts, twenty of these had made serious attempts and their lives were saved by fortuitous and almost miraculous intervention. Possibly some of these twenty had sought to communicate a need for help, but it was obvious on even superficial interviewing that the other fifty-five had used the suicide attempt or gesture as a desperate and often dramatic cry for help. They had anticipated that the cry would be heard and that somebody would come to rescue them from a "sea of troubles."

Although emphasizing the "appeal for help" motive in many cases of attempted suicide in contradistinction to an action aiming only at death, death is nevertheless in the individual's thoughts before, during and after the attempt.[16] This attitude dominates the psychological reactions of the human environment. Any physician who has been involved in the treatment of a patient who has just attempted suicide can remember vividly how death seemed to permeate the whole atmosphere. Although only an attempt, it is a form of death and also survival. This is a strong stimulus for a renewal and revision of human relations on the part of those concerned. Our society rates life and health above all other values and holds as a basic moral tenet the mutual responsibility of individual and group for each other. Thus, suicidal acts can be looked upon as events in the course of the struggle for adjustment.

My interviews with patients who have attempted suicide confirm the impressions of others, that most attempts appear to be made in such a way that an intervention by others seems possible and often probable. Thus such behavior can best be

---

[16] This is described well by E. Stengel: "If one had to design a pictorial symbol for attempted suicide, one would present this act as Janus-faced with one aspect directed towards destruction and death, and the other, towards human contact and life." "Inquiries into Attempted Suicides," *Proceedings of the Royal Society of Medicine*, XLV (1952), 618.

understood when it is related to the human environment. This view accords with the psychoanalytical concept concerning the suicidal act, which is usually regarded as a manifestation of aggression against human objects with whom the individual has identified himself, or as an attempt at union with a deceased person. Since no relationship is free from ambivalence, it is not surprising to find, also, in the act of suicide manifestations of both social and destructive tendencies, of love and hate. The outcome depends on the degree to which each of these tendencies is present, but also on the response of the human environment, provided the latter is given an opportunity to intervene. The way in which the community responds, with its ambivalences of love and hate, has much to do with the final outcome of a suicide attempt. This is stressed because of its vital significance in preventing repeated attempts at suicide, and also because it brings into focus this phenomenon as a challenge for public health and preventive medicine.

Organized efforts of suicide prevention go back to the beginning of this century. Many of the agencies which once existed are no longer in existence, but fortunately, in certain instances, their functions have been taken over by similar agencies.

In the United States such cities as Boston, Miami, and Los Angeles have developed interesting and effective programs of prevention and rescue. The Suicide Prevention Center in Los Angeles is receiving a great deal of recognition for its outstanding work in service to the public and in research. It was founded in 1958. Certain church-related agencies have been active in prevention, also.

In practically all of the large cities of the United States there are certain ministers with special interests and skills in handling suicide candidates, and they have made themselves known directly or indirectly to the public and are called upon frequently for help.

Almost every large hospital in existence has an emergency clinic, and this clinic serves as a ready source of help for the potential suicide. These emergency clinics are widely used, although they seldom advertise as specializing in any way or having any particular interest in suicide prevention.

The same can be said for many agencies and professional people. Most clergymen and physicians are usually available for giving help to those in trouble. As for the specific suicide prevention agencies, the general assumption today is that they serve extremely useful, indeed vital, functions, and that they hold promise of providing at least partial answers to questions about self-destruction, concerning which adequate documentation is at present lacking.

Abolish the Misconceptions

We have a major responsibility to correct commonly believed "facts" about suicide, each one of which is, in reality, false or only partly true. These misconceptions constitute a kind of mythology or folklore of suicide. The first step in prevention is to clarify these misconceptions. Some contain no truth, while others contain a considerable amount. It is easy to see how people will grasp these confusing and, at times, erroneous principles as "rules of the road" in an effort to understand the complex phenomenon of suicide.

A leading misconception is that suicide is always a symptom of mental illness. Even though it is common knowledge that among schizophrenics and patients with affective disorders, such as psychologically depressed patients or those in a manic phase, suicide is not uncommon, there are many situations in which mental illness is not related to the motive in suicide. The Japanese cultural acceptance of hara-kiri refutes such a belief. In the Far East the concept of "saving face" is often the central motivating factor in suicide. Injured insufferably, a recourse to committing suicide at the enemy's doorstep is not infrequently carried out. To some extent the same principle underlay the extreme actions of the Kamikazi pilots of World War II. Malinowski tells how Trobriand Islanders deal with an egregious insult. The injured person climbs a high palm tree, harangues his listeners on the evils of his enemy and the wrong which he has done, and then dives headfirst to his death.[17] Also, in some parts of Polynesia and Melanesia, one may put one's lover to shame for his fickleness by jumping off the highest palm tree. Suttee was a practice of culturally sanctioned homicide in India, dating back to the fourth century B.C., wherein the burning of a Hindu widow took place on her husband's funeral pyre. It became a form of culturally sanctioned suicide when the widow, to prove that she had been a true and faithful wife, requested suttee.

In the study of Farberow and Shneidman of over 700 genuine suicide notes, the authors state that although the feelings expressed were often intense, disturbed, and varied at the time of the suicidal act, just as frequently the quality of reasoning, judgment, and logic expressed was sound, provided the basic premises were accepted.[18]

Another misconception is that suicide is rare among Negroes. Although the suicide rate among Negroes in the United States is only one third to one half of that among whites, when 4 to 5 per 100,000 commit suicide, this number does not permit us to use the term "rare."

Also the factor of strong religious beliefs as an effective check against suicide has lulled some physicians and clergymen into complacency. I have often heard, in emergency clinics or other situations, a staff member say that he does not believe a particular individual will commit suicide, for he is a devoutly religious person, a strong Roman Catholic, etc. If one acts on this assumption he may fail to answer the cry for help of the suicidal patient and thus lose him. Even though Roman Catholics have a lower suicide incidence than Protestants, the severity of the stigma of suicide may cause the truth to be hidden at times. Priests, rabbis, and ministers of all denominations have committed, and do commit, suicide. It is generally accepted that the particular feelings about taking one's life in orthodox Judaism

[17] Bronislaw Malinowski, *Sexual Life of Savages* (New York: Halcyon House, 1929).

[18] *The Cry for Help*, ed. N. L. Farberow and E. S. Shneidman (New York: McGraw-Hill, 1961).

has permeated this religious group to such an extent that it has the lowest suicide incidence among the three major faiths. The Roman Catholics have the second lowest, and this would seem to be related to their strict church policy regarding suicide. The Protestants have the highest incidence of the three groups. Thus, although strong religious beliefs may act at times as a check against the suicidal impulse, we should not neglect such a person in our efforts toward prevention.

Another misconception is that mentally defectives are too dumb to commit suicide. Statistical information at this point is not readily available, however one's clinical experience with suicide patients would lead him to reject the misconception.

The fact that children commit suicide is so unacceptable to adults that one can readily understand the existence of the belief that children do not commit suicide. Another reason why suicide has been overlooked in children and adolescents is the erroneous concept that youngsters do not experience depression. Often they do not exhibit the signs and symptoms of adult depressive reactions but rather other symptoms. The child's behavioral problems of age six to twelve, such as temper tantrums, disobedience, truancy, a feeling that no one cares, running away from home, accident proneness, masochistic actions, and self-destructive behavior not infrequently indicate depressive feelings. The adolescent may exhibit depression by boredom, restlessness, excessive fatigue, preoccupation with trivia, loss of interest in things, or frantically seeking something new to entertain himself. Often the impulsive acting out of anti-social behavior may help the adolescent escape his depressive feelings.

In the prediction and prevention of suicide, the age factor has particular meaning for two groups—the young and the old. The prime causes of death in children, ages 0 through 5, are accidents, and the proportion of these which are truly accidental is generally conceded to be overwhelmingly large. Quite a number are not accidental. While the predominant agents involved in true accidents in children are ingested toxic substances, purposive accidents like suicides rarely involve ingestions, but are generally characterized by extreme violence. According to

Bender and Schilder, the methods used by children in their suicidal wishes and attempts involve jumping out of a window, cutting, stabbing, or hanging oneself, and running in front of speeding automobiles.[19] Older children, however, tend to ingest poisons. If the impression that children who commit suicide are essentially creatures of violence is confirmed by studies presently under way, basic precautions would then have to be directed against violent forms of self-extinction rather than the more adult method of ingesting toxic substances.[20]

Since spite is an overtly expressed emotion in threatened, attempted, and successful suicides in the young, a preventive measure would be to observe carefully and critically strong, hostile, and aggressive emotions and their causes and eliminate them where possible and, if impossible, then control them. Depression associated with separation from parents or loved ones is another major factor in suicidal attempts in the young. Whether the separation is temporary, or complete as in death, if it is viewed as permanent or irrevocable by the child it may be highly traumatizing and may precipitate a suicidal attempt. Public education regarding the pathogenic nature of separation in children is gravely needed. During adolescence, when young people appear to be in a constant state of flux, and when there are marked shifts in mood and the rapid and sometimes violent appearance of anxiety and tension states, suicide may be attempted as the means of resolving unbearable conflicts and problems. There is widespread ignorance and misinformation about the adolescent period of life, and health education regarding the adolescent directed toward parents and teachers would be a major contribution toward improved mental health. Balser and Masterson[21] express an interesting opinion that whereas in adults the relationship between affective disorders and suicide has been established,

[19] Bender and Schilder, op. cit.

[20] J. Hirsh, "Suicide: Predictability and Prevention," Mental Hygiene, XLIV (1960), 382-89.

[21] B. H. Balser and J. F. Masterson, "Suicide in Adolescents," American Journal of Psychiatry, CXVI (1959), 400-401.

in adolescents it would seem that this relationship exists between schizophrenic reactions and suicide.

Another misconception is that those who talk about suicide never go any further than talk.[22] This is false; a person's discussing suicide is a danger sign and may be a desperate plea on his part for help. There seems to be a tendency to give a warning of the impending event and to give others an opportunity to intervene. This warning is also a powerful threat, and if it is not heard or is overlooked the patient may then take action.

Then, above all, one should not heed the common counsel of avoiding direct questioning about suicide, out of fear that suggestions will be put into the patient's mind. Leading questions should be asked. Often the patient's ability to talk about his suicidal impulses may be a form of emotional catharsis and give considerable relief.

Another misconception is that the threat of criminal proceedings has a preventive effect on suicide and attempted suicide. Statistical studies are not especially helpful at this point, because of the many factors influencing the incidence of suicide. Suicide ceased to be a criminal offense on the European continent during the second half of the eighteenth century, but remained one in England. English suicide rates are lower than on the continent; but one can speculate that the tendency toward concealment would be greater in England than elsewhere, owing to the legal status of suicide. In Scotland, where legislation is in keeping with the continent, the suicide rates are lower than in England.[23] It has been pointed out that legislation against sui-

---

[22] The error of this view is further strengthened by a recent study conducted in St. Louis. One hundred thirty-four consecutive suicides were studied by means of systematic interviews with family, in-laws, job associates, friends, physicians, and ministers a short time after the suicide. It was found that 69 per cent of the suicides had communicated suicidal ideas, and that 41 per cent had specifically stated that they intended to commit suicide. The study also revealed that in the majority of instances, the suicidal communications were recent in origin, repeatedly verbalized, and expressed to many persons. E. Robins, et. al., "The Communication of Suicidal Intent," *American Journal of Psychiatry*, CXV (1959), 724-33.

[23] The suicide rates for England in 1951, 1952, and 1953 were 13.2 for men and 6.8 for women. The corresponding rates for Scotland were 7.7 and 3.4 respectively. Stengel and Cook, op. cit.

cide may have two opposite effects. A person may make a more serious attempt so that he will really kill himself and not fall within the clutches of the law; or persons who have made unsuccessful suicide attempts may be discouraged and frightened from seeking proper advice and treatment, with the result that there is again an increase in actual number of suicides.

Historically, suicide was considered a capital crime for many centuries. Even in the eighteenth century in some countries there were executions of dead people who died by their own hands.[24] The bodies were dragged into court and out to the place of execution by the feet, face down, picking up the dust and mud of the streets and getting mutilated against the cobblestone pavements. These judicial punitive measures proved highly ineffective.

The statement that suicide is the "curse of the poor" or the "disease of the rich" is controversial but conceded to contain some truth. Some social and economic authorities seem to indicate that the suicide toll varies almost exclusively with socioeconomic status, thus relating suicide to the struggles of the poor and to the ennui of the rich. Other investigators indicate that almost all social and economic strata contribute their pro rata share to the overall suicide rate.

Another misconception is that suicide and depression are synonymous. One often hears the statement, "I cannot understand his killing himself, for he did not act as if he were unhappy or depressed." This points to the commonly mistaken belief that suicide occurs only when depression is present. Suicides have taken place during agitation and anxiety, psychoses, organic impairment, or other symptoms. While depression does remain the best single indication of potential suicide, there are also other roads to suicide than the avenue of depression.

Improvement after a suicidal crisis is considered by many to mean that the suicide risk is over. Investigators and clinicians have observed for some time that persons in a suicidal crisis who subsequently committed suicide, did so within ninety days of

[24] Gregory Zilboorg, *Mind, Medicine, and Man* (New York: Harcourt, Brace and Co., 1943), pp. 246-97.

having passed the emotional crisis and after they had seemed to be on the way to recovery.[25] Thus physicians, relatives, and others should be especially cautious and watchful for at least ninety days after a person has been suicidal and seems to be improving. The uninitiated may confuse improvement with an increase in psychomotor energy.

Another misconception is that people who have previously attempted suicide are dramatic, hysterical, and manipulative personalities and use such patterns without ever having any serious intent. Such a view can be profoundly misleading, for the records show that many patients, possibly around 75 per cent, have previously either attempted or threatened suicide, or both. A good rule of thumb to remember is that individuals who threaten suicide are often more disturbed than people who attempt suicide.

A common belief is that suicide is the result of baseless impulse. The careful observer will recognize that rarely is suicide the result of baseless impulse. It is almost always the culmination of a process or set of circumstances of long duration. This complex phenomenon, especially in its origins, lends itself to intervention and treatment.

The Danger Signs in the Potential Suicide

The next major step in suicide prevention is a recognition of danger signs and certain host factors which make their appearance in the suicide process. Although these cannot be regarded as precise predictors, they must be considered in programs of prevention and treatment of suicide. Since suicide is rarely an impulsive, highly agitated, unpremeditated act, but is generally a well-defined, deliberate act, these factors have real significance in evaluating a clinical case.

The first of these signs is the presence of depression, especially with agitation, but any depression is dangerous and the patient

---

[25] *Clues to Suicide,* ed. E. S. Shneidman and N. L. Farberow (New York: McGraw-Hill, 1957).

can be suicidal. The proper management of the depressed patient is outside the scope of this discussion. I feel constrained, however, to mention briefly one of the serious symptoms of depression—insomnia. When the patient awakens long before his time to arise—for example, around 4:00 A.M.—he is an excellent candidate for suicide. The psychodynamics of depression have already been discussed. In the simplest form the depressive spell of the adult is related to the depressive spell of the infant. The person simply says, "I have no mother and no father. What have I done to cause me to lose them? I must seek some kind of forgiveness in order to get them back." Then the person begins to make proper restitution and atonement through various types of maneuvering for forgiveness.

The next danger sign is a past history of a suicide attempt. This offers a major field for preventive work. Many will repeat the attempt. In fact, the magnitude of the suicide problem must be measured in the *attempts* at suicide made each year. Estimates based on hospital and police records indicate that at least five and as many as sixty attempts are made for every successful one completed. These attempts, which are costly, cruel, and tragic, are the real measure of the specter of suicide. Stengel's studies show that the risk of suicide (the fatal suicide act) is far higher among those with a history of a suicidal attempt than in the general population.[26] The outlook for elderly people who attempt suicide but do not succeed is generally much poorer than that of younger people. Reports of British and American psychiatrists indicate that 12 per cent of those who attempt suicide in old age will make a second try and succeed within two years.[27]

Where there is a family history of suicide, the physician should put a great deal of credence on the possibility of suicide.

A danger sign of importance is where there is an overwhelming pattern of preoccupation with death and the desire to die.

[26] E. Stengel, "Recent Research into Suicide and Attempted Suicide," American Journal of Psychiatry, CXVIII (1962), 725-27.
[27] P. O'Neal, E. Robins, and E. H. Schmidt, "A Psychiatric Study of Attempted Suicides in Persons Over Sixty Years of Age," Archives of Neurology and Psychiatry, LXXV (1956), 275-84.

The patient not infrequently speaks of this preoccupation spontaneously. If he does not and the physician, clergyman, or relative is concerned as to whether this type of ideation exists, then the patient should be questioned regarding it.

Frequent and recurrent communication of suicidal ideas and fantasies, with specific or non-specific statements of intent, are of grave import.

The incidence of suicide increases precipitously in the older age group. In the United States the suicide incidence rises steadily from its relatively low point to an alarming peak of over 50 per 100,000 population in age groups over 75.

There appear to be specific age and sex patterns of attempting and committing suicide against which appropriate measures may be taken. These patterns have already been discussed.

Susceptibility to suicide is lowest among those who have some family ties, religious, occupational, and community relationships. Unmarried individuals (single, widowed, or divorced) generally have higher suicide rates than married people.

The time of day, season of the year, and weather conditions appear to influence suicide rates. Though certain of these factors have been frequently observed in relationship to suicide, practically no careful studies have yet been done. However, one such extensive study is being carried out at the present time at the Veterans Administration Hospital, Houston, Texas. As has already been noted, for people in depression the early morning hours may be critical from a suicidal point of view. A drop in barometric pressure and certain other weather conditions are often associated with an increased incidence of suicide.

The so-called "anniversary syndrome" may be a trigger mechanism for those who are depressed and potentially suicidal. The anniversary of sad events, such as a broken engagement, divorce, or death of a loved one, is a special *Ides* for depressives of all ages, male or female. Two opposite phenomena have been generally observed in this matter. In one group of cases, as the anniversary date approaches, there may be no overt recognition, no mention of the fact by the person in the depression and this may be a warning sign in itself. The potential suicide candidate may go about his business as usual, and, then, on the anniversary—almost always on the date or on the day of the week itself —destroy himself. In other groups there is a steady deepening of the depression, climaxing in suicide on the anniversary day or date.

Utilization of Resources, and Approaches in Suicide Prevention

Facilities should be available so that every person who has attempted suicide could have a psychiatric evaluation and definitive treatment. Many hospitals have a plan whereby every patient brought to the emergency clinic who has made any kind of suicide attempt, no matter how minor, must be evaluated by the resident psychiatrist as part of the disposition of the patient. If it appears that the patient made only a manipulative gesture and his physical condition is satisfactory, he is allowed to go home after counseling with him and his family. The patient is given an early appointment to the outpatient psychiatry clinic or referred to a private psychiatrist. If the patient made a genuine attempt, he is hospitalized for psychiatric evaluation and treatment. Often physicians do not feel the same concern for suicide as for medical or surgical fatalities. There is some tendency to feel that suicide is the individual's own business, and that he has a right to die if he wishes. Most physicians and clergymen have heard patients say, "If I want to die, I should be allowed to. After all, this is a free country." I have generally responded to such questions as honestly as I could, by saying: "You may be right, and I can see how you may hold this view. I respect your courage and your effort to find a solution to circumstances which seem to be overwhelming you. However, I do feel there is a better solution than terminating your life, and I am committed both personally and professionally to helping you find this better solution."

All threats or gestures of suicide, whether spoken of in jest, or seemingly insincere, should never be lightly dismissed. Although the patient may not carry out the threat, almost everyone who does commit suicide has given some earlier warning of his intention.

Lay persons must be trained to do preventive work. The development of suicide prevention centers and organizations of various types where a person with suicidal thoughts or intentions can turn is a hopeful sign for the present and future. Often suicide occurs when a patient seems almost recovered from a depression. Physicians are aware of this, and in spite of apprising families of this hazard, patients are often signed out of hospitals against medical advice and forthwith commit suicide within hours after leaving. A recent example of this was a patient in the depths of a suicidal depression whom I admitted to a hospital. After several days of therapy he began to improve, and his wife signed him out of the hospital against medical advice. The psychiatrist on call that night tried in vain for over two hours to convince the wife that this was exactly the wrong time for the patient to leave the hospital, for in the depths of his depression he was not able to even organize a method of destroying himself. Now he had sufficiently improved so that he would be quite capable of planning and performing the act. The wife refused to listen because of conscious and unconscious factors which are not within the scope of this discussion. Shortly after the patient left the hospital, his car was found parked on a river bridge, and three days later his body was recovered from the river.

Especially is it appropriate to comment on the role of the clergyman in suicide prevention. When in trouble, many people automatically turn to their church for consolation and guidance. The wise pastor, counseling in his study, does much to help banish the burden of guilt, anger, and depression. The priest, through the confessional, offers God's forgiveness and a new beginning. This is a ministry of healing, and its value in restoring equilibrium to the troubled, one can estimate, is beyond measure.

Public education is of great importance in preventing suicide. We are still restrained by prejudice and other factors in our efforts to provide effective psychiatric treatment. Mental illness is generally considered disgraceful, and those who try to commit suicide are often considered weak and useless. The danger signals of suicide should be widely publicized. Mental hygiene clinics could greatly aid by accepting this particular program and giving educational help. Public health workers should endeavor to be the leaders in health education as related to suicide prevention.

An even more crucial step in suicide prevention is the rigorous training of parents and teachers in the principles of mental hygiene. Learning how to handle a crisis in one's own life and also learning how to help others during their crisis periods are worthy mental health goals for all of us. It is a safe assumption that a high suicide rate among specific groups in certain populations is expressive of a lack of mental stability and mental health. If this is true, it behooves all of us to work for a high level of emotional health in our society, for the healthy person is better equipped for problem-solving in an effective and constructive manner in keeping with the value system in his cultural group.

Police officers should have ample instruction on how to deal with suicidal attempts. This should include not only how to give emergency first aid, but also how to procure psychiatric evaluation and help families to procure it. An excellent educational film for the police is *Cry for Help*, produced by Lloyd Rowland and the Louisiana Mental Health Association.

The legal and medical professions should work for stricter controls and legal restraints over the promiscuous prescribing of lethal and addictive drugs, particularly barbiturates. Even the laws which exist regarding the use of barbiturates are not well enforced in this country.

Hospital administrators and boards of trustees should accept their responsibility to include adequate, complete psychiatric consultation and follow-up treatment of all persons brought into hospital emergency clinics because of attempted suicide.

Registration of suicidal attempts and the reporting of such attempts to the state health department should be required in the same way as reportable diseases, with follow-up supervision by public health doctors and nurses in order to see that the patient is receiving psychiatric and medical care.

Psychiatrists, other medical practitioners, clergymen, and others seeing suicide patients should keep adequate case records in order to increase our understanding of the various motives and thus help with prevention. The study of clinical case material furnishes us with the richest resources for unraveling the hidden facets of suicide. Life and accident insurance companies should be encouraged to carry out research in suicide prevention. These companies contribute large sums for research to prolong life in such diseases as cardiovascular and kidney disease, gastrointestinal illnesses, accidents, and many others, but so far the companies have shown little interest in suicide prevention. Possibly these companies could be encouraged to carry out and finance psychiatric research and lay education.

Summary

This discussion has focused on the phenomenon of suicide as a major frontier in community mental health.

In the soliloquy from Hamlet, Shakespeare speaks pointedly to the issue involved in this discussion:

> To be, or not to be: that is the question;
> Whether 'tis nobler in the mind to suffer
> The slings and arrows of outrageous fortune,
> Or to take arms against a sea of troubles,
> And by opposing end them? To die: to sleep;
> No more; and by a sleep to say we end
> The heart-ache and the thousand natural shocks
> That flesh is heir to, 'tis a consummation
> Devoutly to be wish'd.

Only two alternatives are offered in these dramatic lines. One has a choice of accepting and bearing his sufferings or of taking up arms against his troubles, and end them by dying. There is a third alternative, not mentioned, and that is coming to grips with one's problems with the help of medical, religious, and social groups and solving them through present, known techniques. It is the task of society today to accept the challenge of this dramatic crisis presented by the suicidal patient and to offer him health resources which will enable him to translate a wish to die into a wish to live. Furthermore, we are challenged to offer him assistance in developing personal skills in self-understanding and the handling of the vicissitudes of life so that he will have no need of solving his problems through self-destructive measures.

An acceptance of this goal will push our task far beyond that of efficacious intervention with suicidal patients and beyond the detection and measurement of the suicidal potential in an individual. This is as it should be, for health encompasses much more than the absence of symptoms.

8

False Pregnancy in a Male

Today the meaning of illness is attracting widespread attention among students of human behavior. As will be discussed in the chapter entitled "Partners in Healing," the question is asked: "What do these symptoms tell us about this patient, his family, and his community?" One may also ask what this patient is trying to communicate to others about his emotional and spiritual condition.

I have chosen for this chapter the story of a patient who incorporated religious factors in his struggle for health. In his illness he distorted reality, and many of his distortions spilled over into the religious area. He assumed a messianic role as part of a grandiose psychic repair, an effort to heal himself, as revealed by his symptoms.

The Patient's Story

A thirty-three-year-old seaman was seen in a private diagnostic clinic. He gave a history of having had the following symptoms for six to eight weeks: abdominal distention, morning nausea, movement felt in the abdomen, and increased appetite after the onset of abdominal swelling. The physician, who examined him carefully, thought there was possibly some fluid in the abdomen. He noted the rather marked abdominal distention, and the patient reported that his waist had increased from thirty-two to thirty-seven inches. The physician felt that these symptoms were suggestive of liver disease and questioned the patient about his drinking habits. The patient gave a history of practically no alcohol intake. Acute infectious hepatitis was considered. Many

129

laboratory procedures were done, including urine, hematologic, and blood chemistry studies. All were within normal limits. Radiographic studies, including a flat film of the abdomen, GI series, and barium enema were negative.

Physical examination revealed a well-developed white male who appeared his stated age. The abdomen was large and protuberant, and seemed out of proportion for his muscular build.

The physician reported to the patient that all the studies were negative. He mentioned that he had seriously considered liver disease but had come to the conclusion that the symptoms were related to some kind of functional gastrointestinal disturbance. The patient then said, "I don't think it is that." The physician asked him what he thought was wrong. The patient replied, "I think there is life in my abdomen. This may be a pregnancy." The physician, taken aback by this pronouncement, told the patient his case would be studied further.

At this point I was consulted.

When the patient came for his first psychiatric appointment, he was anxious at the beginning of the interview but relaxed very soon. He related with warmth, and the therapist had no difficulty empathizing with him.

The beginning part of the first session is reported to give a feeling for the patient's symptomatology:

Therapist: I am glad you were able to come, and I would like you to tell me something about the development of your present symptoms or what we might call your present state of health.

Patient: The doctor said I had a nervous condition in my bowel. Studies have been done on my urine and my blood. X-rays were taken. It all added up to a nervous condition in the bowel, according to my doctor.

Therapist: Well, tell me how your symptoms began.

Patient: I was lying out in the sunshine and I had this peculiar feeling in my abdomen. I watched my toilet for bleeding. I noticed none. I went to the ship's doctor and told him about the movements in my abdomen. He gave me some vitamins. Later on he put me in the hospital before the ship arrived in Rio de Janeiro. I rested and read. Later I came back to port in the United States and then finally went to a private medical clinic.

Therapist: What was your job on the ship?

Patient: I was a bellboy or waiter. I did not do my best job on this last voyage because I was somewhat preoccupied with my health.

Therapist: What do you think is wrong?

Patient: A vague feeling began in my mind while aboard ship that I was going to have a child. I am an ardent believer. With God all things are possible. I have had morning nausea with some gagging. No pain. Nothing would come up. Especially did I have nausea after morning coffee. Since I have been back from sea, I was helping a lady move some household furniture. I felt very definite movement in my abdomen. Then I decided for sure it was a form of life. It seemed incredible but the thought came back to me over and over again. I am in a state of suspense. What is it? It could not be fat because I have gained no weight and I am not fat anywhere else.

Therapist: What is your attitude toward having a baby?

Patient: It leaves me without explanation—that a miracle has happened. Recently when one of the doctors was examining me in the abdomen, trying to feel my liver or something, I received a warning that this doctor was applying too much pressure. I felt flushed. I thought maybe he may harm whatever life was in my abdomen. I have been trying to take care of myself physically and have been taking prenatal vitamins.

Therapist: What about the delivery of this baby?

Patient: I don't know. I have made no preparation in my thinking. I suppose a cesarean section would be the only way.

Therapist: Tell me about your sexual orientation or interests.

Patient: I have been with both sexes. I lean toward the masculine. I have tried to find out why. I yearn for the same sex. I think it goes back to my religious teaching. Our picture of God through the Bible is that he is a male figure. God is a man. His first and preferable creature was a man. Man has always been the most desired of the two sexes, so I have chosen the strongest. Having known both sexes, I feel most secure and contented with the male sex. To tell you the truth, I have no strong drives for either heterosexual or homosexual activity.

Therapist: Are you comfortable with your sexual orientation?

Patient: I held many conversations with the ship's doctor about my sexual problems. I often wonder what I am, who I am, and why.

Therapist: How would you feel if it turned out that you were really going to have a baby and this could be proven medically?
Patient: Delighted. Delighted. Delighted.

The patient always wore his trousers open at the top. His trousers were all new in appearance, but he was unable to zip them up because of the increase in the size of his abdomen. Lack of money kept him from buying a new wardrobe. He wore the tail of his sport shirt outside of his belt. This covered his unzipped trousers and gave the appearance of a maternity smock. He appeared strong, healthy, and masculine.

After a few sessions with the patient, he revealed the fact that one of his close friends aboard ship had begun talking of getting married and having a child. The patient felt rejected and began to wish that he could give his friend the child the friend wanted. His symptoms began shortly thereafter. He became convinced that he was pregnant. Since this was something unique in physiological history, he began to endow his experience with special significance. A part of the interview material is given verbatim to show the meaning of the patient's symptoms for himself and society:

Therapist: Tell me why you, a man, should be pregnant.
Patient: I thought God may use me in a special way in his work. All things are possible through God. After I felt I was pregnant, I began to think about the meaning of this pregnancy for myself and for society.
Therapist: So you began exploring what this could mean; why this was happening to you; what would result from this. This explains some of your spectacular ideas.
Patient: Yes, I would argue both sides. I always seek a meaning. Finally, I stopped being too introspective. Afraid I would end up behind bars in a mental institution. Yet, if I could be used for something remarkable and grand, something wonderful, if in the process of this thing I would die, it would not matter. The idea is strongly implanted in me, and I don't know how to turn loose of the idea.
Therapist: You don't know what will be left if you turn loose. You now feel caught up in some great purpose and if this great pur-

pose is taken away, what will be left of you but your loneliness. Is this what you mean?

Patient: Yes. Maybe it is happening to teach me something. Exactly what, I don't know. Where did I get this big idea? God creates from nothing, so if one believes in miracles, such a task would not be too difficult for him. For I believe still in miracles of the spirit if not of the flesh. This is all tied up with my idea of seeing love prevail and not hate. I want my love to live, to be creative and not destructive. This atomic age seems to be hastening toward destruction.

Therapist: You are saying that you want your love and your human relationships to be creative. You fear world destruction and if you could do something to prevent this you would, even if it cost you your life.

Patient: Yes. Man always seeks a why. All of us are counted—have some definite purpose. So anyone could be singled out for a specific purpose. Some such tasks are difficult. Wonder who would want to be singled out for such a task as being pregnant, especially if he is a male.

Therapist: I do not feel you are unhappy for being chosen for what is happening to you.

Patient: But I am very lonely. I have been lonely before. It is so easy to slip into self-pity. Somebody has to be chosen to develop, to withstand the destruction of the atom bomb. Somebody to perpetuate life. Against fire and radiation, how could one live? My thoughts here are all a fantastic dream. The entire world and at least all life on the face of the globe may be destroyed by our fooling around with atomic energy and the radiation which results. If somebody could be born or developed in some way to be resistant to atomic energy and radiation, the race could be perpetuated in the face of man's destructive tendencies. If God would bring to life certain people with resistant qualities, the race would continue.

Therapist: Maybe you are so hoping for man to survive his destructive tendencies and the atom bomb and radiation that your hopes are creating a fantastic dream that you or the child will have a part in this survival.

Patient: Yes, but he will be saved only by love. Out of love will come salvation.

Therapist: It seems that what has happened has grown out of your need and hope.

Patient: I agree that what is happening to me has grown out of my needs and hopes, but it probably won't lead to happiness. But Christ was not always happy. Many people who make contributions in philosophy and art and in other areas are unhappy.

Personal History

The patient is very uncertain of his own background. He has no recollection of his mother and believes she died when he was very young. Once his father told him that he was adopted. He thinks that his father could have been kidding. Yet, the patient often expressed the childlike fantasy that he was probably adopted, that probably his true parents were of royal heritage. He made many efforts to get an official birth certificate but never succeeded. He was reared by his alcoholic father and a series of stepmothers. Often he and his father lived alone for months. Then a new stepmother would appear in their home. Some of these women treated him well and others poorly. He wonders now if his father were really married to these women or had them as mistresses. He always felt inadequate and unaccepted by his father and these women. He longed for his father's acceptance and strength. There were no other siblings in the family.

He attended both public and parochial schools. His father moved so often that he seldom remained more than a semester in any school. He developed close ties with many of his teachers and felt grieved when he had to move away with his father. No long-lasting friendships were developed among classmates because of his transiency, according to the patient. His favorite subjects were art and science.

As for sexual development, he remembers sex play with boys and girls his age when he was five and six. A resurgence of this began again when he was nine and again when he was twelve. At fifteen he began dating and indulged in petting but made no effort to engage in sexual intercourse until the age of twenty.

He claims to have had heterosexual and homosexual experiences. He lived with a divorcee for several months and, according to his report, performed adequately sexually. Gradually through the years, beginning with puberty, his interest in men has grown. He does not describe this as a craving but a desire to share their company.

When the boy was sixteen he was taken from the custody of his father and placed in a boarding home by the juvenile court. This decision was made by the court because of the father's alcoholism.

Since World War II he has been a seaman in the Merchant Marine Service. He is fond of the sea. He is able to read widely and continue a program of self-education. He looks upon himself as a self-appointed diplomat to all foreign ports of call.

While in port, he has lived with the same family for the past few years. The landlady has accepted him as a son, and he looks upon her as a mother. The relationship is a warm one, and on a few occasions she came with the patient to see the therapist.

A few of his philosophical ideas are given to point out some of his major concerns.

He considers himself a pacifist. He witnessed the Japanese attack on Pearl Harbor. Throughout the war, when he worked in a Navy yard, he saw a steady stream of half-destroyed ships and wounded men come through. He began to contemplate war, a nation's guilt or innocence, a man's possessiveness. These are his words:

Japan was provoked out of economic necessity. I have visited Japan, Italy, and Germany and found the people no more vicious than we are. A prominent Russian philosopher, Nicolas Berdyaev, once stated that in the Old Testament story of Cain and Abel, one other question should have been asked. God spoke to Cain and said, "Cain, where is thy brother Abel?" He should have then turned to the slain Abel and asked, "Abel, where is thy brother Cain?" This philosopher is saying what I believe, that both the victor and the victim must share the blame for a criminal act.

Although he is not active in any church, he looks upon himself as a devout believer. He stated that he once wore a cross around his neck but feels such an outward display to be inappropriate and in most instances insincere:

135

In some sections of the world I saw great cathedrals with golden crosses and altars, and these cathedrals were surrounded by hungry, ragged, ignorant children. I am sure such displeases God no end. He wants bread in children's stomachs before he wants bread and gold on any altar. The temple of the human body is more beautiful than a man-made temple. And if to build a temple, children's health and happiness are jeopardized, then we sin grievously. Display the cross? No. The finest place to wear it is in the heart.

A few of the authors he frequently quoted were Albert Schweitzer, Aldous Huxley, and Kahlil Gibran.

His attitude toward women deserves special attention. He felt that the women in his father's life failed his father as well as himself. The patient felt that they had never accepted him. He often implied that he would like to be the type of woman that his father should have had—that any man should really have. Such a woman would protect and care for a man.

He looked upon himself as a woman in a man's body and expressed the belief that the "female hormone" was dominant in him rather than the male.

His only avenue of expression of womanhood has been through some form of homosexuality. He has attempted to act toward men as he wanted a mother to act toward him. He has never wanted to wear women's clothes or jewelry or to dress in other ways like a woman. He feels that a man in woman's clothes looks ridiculous. He has considered having his genitals amputated but decided this would not make him a woman but only a castrated male. He expressed it this way: "If under the surgeon's knife I could become a woman, that would be fine— but I know better. I would be just a castrated male in woman's clothes. Thus I must accept what I really am—a woman in a man's body." His ideal woman is the Japanese type, "for the women of Japan have been taught for centuries the true art of taking care of the man."

Diagnosis

The patient functioned so well that one would not suspect any difficulty, unless he discussed his delusion. Psychological tests were administered by two psychologists, who reported no evidence of an integrative defect.

He appeared oriented in all spheres at all times except about himself. He was well controlled and carried on intelligent and sensible discussions about many subjects. His practical knowledge and self-education far exceeded that suggested by his formal training. (He did not finish high school.)

At this stage diagnosis is difficult. The psychosomatic manifestations of his false pregnancy suggest a hysterical overlay. The patient is paranoid, but whether this is an episode to cover a bizarre situation (pseudocyesis in a male) or part of a more malignant process is difficult to say. It is conceivable that the patient went through the initial stages of paranoid development, which for the time being might have been stopped due to intensive psychotherapy.

Although he gave up his delusion while in treatment (the details of this will be discussed later), it seems unlikely that this turn to recovery is definitive. It is much more likely that sooner or later the old delusions will flare up again and flourish, possibly with new ones. One is even faced with the question as to whether he is not dealing already with a schizophrenic. The basic delusion is very absurd, although its elaboration appears to be logical. Yet how much of this logic is due not so much to the patient's own thought as to the dialogue between him and the physician is a moot question. One might object that the ease with which contact could be made with the patient speaks against his being a schizophrenic.

There isn't enough evidence to consider seriously transvestism tendencies.[1] He felt he was a woman in a man's body. Although he had no desire to wear women's clothes and jewelry, he had become preoccupied with a woman's domain—giving birth to a baby. Although he had considered having his genitals amputated, he discarded this approach to solving his problem, stating that such would not make him a woman. Thus he did not seek to be regarded as a woman by society, to be called by a woman's

---

[1] C. Hamburger, et. al., "Transvestism: Hormonal, Psychiatric, and Surgical Treatment," *Journal of the American Medical Association*, CXLV (1953), 391.

name, and to occupy himself with womanly tasks other than the birth process.

The patient's conflict over his homosexuality is obvious. Only a diagnostic impression should be ventured at this time. The development of a schizophrenic process, paranoid in type, is postulated.

Meaning of His Symptoms

The patient's image of himself is that of a lonely person who is seeking a mission in life to give special meaning to his own existence. He is not certain of his own identity. He knew only a single parent, and his efforts to obtain a birth certificate or a hospital record of his birth were all in vain.

He looks upon himself as a woman in a man's body. He has used homosexuality as a way of expressing his feminine tendencies.

His feelings of inadequacy are clearly seen. It is obvious that his father never accepted him and that he has longed for his father's acceptance and strength. There is ample evidence of this in the interview material.

His yearning for the male, then, represents deep dependency needs, wherein he seeks through a close male relationship to appropriate the strength of the male. The nuclear problem is homosexuality.[2]

In making a grandiose repair, it appears as though this patient in his messianic role had attempted to identify himself with the mother of a saviour, and the expected child was a saviour.

Treatment Plan and Course

At the beginning of therapy, the question occurred to the therapist whether he should go along with the patient's delusion. An excellent precedent for so doing is the manner in which

[2] Dependency and power components of this patient's motivation are so much stronger than his sexual motivation, possibly pseudohomosexuality should be considered here. See Lionel Ovesey, "Pseudohomosexuality, the Paranoid Mechanism and Paranoia, an Adaptational Revision of a Classical Freudian Theory," *Psychiatry*, XVIII (1955), 163.

Robert Lindner handled the patient described in "The Jet-Propelled Couch." [3] After getting to know the patient, I was certain I should stand for reality. Thus, in reply to direct questions of whether I believed he was pregnant, I replied that I could not see how a man could have a baby. But I always went on to say that the feeling that he was pregnant meant something very special to him and that he could hold on to this idea as long as he needed to do so. [4]

The patient accepted the therapist as a benevolent authority figure and gradually seemed to accept the therapist's explanation regarding the patient's delusional system. Gradually the therapist diverted the patient's attention from the delusion to thinking about himself and talking about other phases of his life experience.

Slowly the delusion of being pregnant was abandoned. He acquired considerable intellectual insight into what had happened to him and apparently also some emotional acceptance and understanding. He was in treatment for about four months. He reached the conclusion that his situation was a classic example of mind over body. He was interested in learning how he could handle strong wishes and stressful periods in the future, so that such a predicament would not overtake him again. He did mention that the mind was so subtle and wise that instead of choosing this type of illness again, it would probably choose something else.

Thus, he may well be ready for another delusional experience or for the resumption of his old one whenever he may need it.

The patient's psychophysiologic symptoms began to subside after two months of psychotherapy. At this stage in treatment he had begun to discuss freely his interpretation of the role for which he had been chosen. By this time he seemed to have ac-

---

[3] The Fifty-Minute Hour (New York: Holt, Rinehart, and Winston, 1955).

[4] David A. Boyd, in discussing the paper by Fried et al., "Study in Gynecology," Journal of the American Medical Association, CXLV (1951), 1329, commented that in treating a woman with pseudocyesis, therapy can be approached only from the standpoint that the patient has developed the symptoms because she needs them. Thus any treatment must be directed toward the total needs of the patient rather than the relief of the presenting symptom.

quired considerable insight into his frustrations and needs. When he began to show some understanding of the relationship of emotions to bodily functions, the therapist noticed for the first time the beginning of a decrease in his symptoms. Improvement continued from this point, and after two months his abdominal distention and movements had subsided, as well as the other symptoms.

Summary

A thirty-three-year-old seaman was treated because he felt he was pregnant. He described symptoms not unlike those of a pregnant female.

As for the diagnosis of the patient, only an impression is ventured at this time: a developing schizophrenic process, paranoid in type.

A motivational formulation was attempted, with homosexuality as the nuclear conflict. Of the three motivational components of homosexuality—sex, power, and dependency—the sexual component appeared the weakest in this patient. He identified with strong male figures in an unconscious effort to appropriate their strength. His struggle for power, coupled with his conflict over socially unacceptable sexual interests, pushed him into a delusion of grandeur as a specific self-reparative effort. The despised one would become the chosen one.

His symptoms began to subside after two months of treatment, and in four months he was almost free of symptoms.

Such a case presentation as this is included in this book because it is a dramatic illustration of how religious factors can be incorporated into one's struggle for health in the face of developing emotional illness. The capacity of the mind to seek equilibrium, meaning, and purpose in life, and to find complete or partial healing is a marvelous testimony to the inner resources for healing in man.

9
Church Phobia

One September Sunday, a thirty-seven-year-old white woman was worshiping in her church and listening to her pastor preach on the subject of doubt. In the pastor's sermon he said, "There are those who have their doubts and they want proof of God." Then suddenly this thought came to her, which she addressed to God: "If you exist, strike me dead to prove it."

The following Sunday she became dizzy in church and almost fainted. Her symptoms were so severe that she left during the service of worship and stayed away from church for almost three years. On the few occasions when she did try to attend, she either had to leave before the service ended or could not get beyond the vestibule. She complained of palpitation of the heart, profuse perspiration, dizziness, and the feeling that she was going to faint. She related these symptoms to a minimal response by God to her challenge. She was afraid that God would fully accept her challenge and give her the proof she had demanded. To save herself she would withdraw from the service of worship when symptoms began to develop.

She reported that if a service of worship was not taking place in the church, she could enter and walk anywhere in the sanctuary without getting a single symptom. When asked to explain this, she replied, "I asked God to prove himself to me while a service was in progress. If God accepts my challenge, I feel that he will do so only during a church service."

During the past three years her symptoms became worse before and during the Christmas Season. She attributed this to the expanded church program during this season and the insistence on the part of her family that she participate. She spoke also of

141

her awareness of the meaning of Christmas and her broken relationship to the church. She went on to say, "It is like grieving over something I have lost, and I am more conscious of this loss during Christmas." Her daily picture was that of a person in mourning.

At the beginning of the third Christmas Season after her challenge to God, she came to me for psychotherapy. She opened the initial interview with the statement that she had lost her faith and could not attend church. She went on, in that session and the following ones, to give frankly and honestly a long history of sexual and religious conflict. It was obvious from the material she related that the sexual and religious spheres impinged on each other at many points.

After her challenge to God, in a variety of places (especially in church) and situations sexual fantasies about Christ would pop into her mind. She would try to replace these bad thoughts with good thoughts. At those times when her doubts were the most intense she found herself thinking repeatedly of Christ and saying to herself rather crude expressions which involved the name of Christ coupled with sexual fantasies. Such thoughts show the tragic bondage of this patient to her illness and her frightening struggle for wholeness.

Sexual History

The patient's attitude toward sex was consistent with her sexual history. Although her parents gave her little sex education, she was urged to behave herself in all sexual matters.

She recalled engaging in all types of sex play, short of intercourse, throughout her entire school years. Guilt feelings followed in the wake of each such experience, along with many nightmares associated with a variety of punishments.

When she was in her early teens, a boy carved on a tree her name, that of her boyfriend, and a slang word for sexual intercourse. She reported her reaction to this incident in these words: "I took the knife from him and chased him. I was very angry. If I had caught him, I would have killed him. I threw the knife at him. It hit him but did not cut him." When asked why she became so upset over this, she replied: "I don't know except that I always hated the crude word he carved on the tree. That word is written many places. It upsets me each time I see it, so I try to avoid it." When I asked her if she felt that the carving of this word in association with her name and that of her boyfriend reflected on her virtue, she answered, "Exactly."

She spoke of having had deep sexual needs all her life and of struggling to deny, suppress, or control these feelings. During therapy she reported dreams filled with her repressed desires for many men. Her brother-in-law, unfaithful to his wife, appeared in her dreams in sexual situations.

When her husband was away from home during World War II, she became romantically involved with her employer. This affair ended short of sexual intercourse, but she felt that she had committed adultery, at least in her heart. She stated her concern in these words, "Since thoughts are as wicked as deeds, I am guilty."

She has been married for eighteen years to an understanding, mature, and attentive husband. They have always gotten along well together, free of any major difficulties. Although there has not been much success in the sexual area, this has not been a serious cause for marital disharmony. The patient enjoyed sex for a brief period after marriage and was at times orgastic. Then she became partially frigid. The sexual act disgusted her, and each time after sexual intercourse she spent a long time in the bathroom bathing herself.

She has never liked to be alone with a man, especially in a private place. (This does not apply to her husband.) She mentioned that from age twelve she tried to avoid ever being alone with her father. She reported this when she was discussing sex, but made no direct reference to having ever had sexual feelings about her father. It was at age twelve that she saw her father with another woman. From then on she felt only sorrow and contempt for him. Her mother was living at that time, but died four years later.

Early Development

This patient was reared in a home in which the family was preoccupied with cleanliness and orderliness. Any breach of truth or honesty resulted in severe punishment. She was toilet trained early and rigidly. As late as age fourteen she was hesitant to spend the night away from home for fear that she might wet the bed. She reported that throughout her adult life she has always emptied her bladder immediately before going to bed because of the same fear.

Her parents were of German extraction. They spoke German in the home only when they wanted to conceal something from the children. Her mother died when the patient was sixteen. Her father died a year before she entered therapy. There were eight girls and two boys in the family. She was the next to the youngest child.

She spoke of her mother as warm and friendly. However, she was not close enough to her to discuss intimate things with her. Her father was mean, autocratic, and quarrelsome. She saw him only at mealtime, since he spent most of his time in the shop which he operated. They were never close to each other.

She married at age nineteen. Her husband was twenty-one. They had only one child, a girl, thirteen years old at the time of therapy. The patient described her present home as a true haven in comparison to the tumultuous home in which she grew up.

Treatment

A psychoanalytically oriented type of psychotherapy was the treatment approach used with her. After several weeks of therapy we began to plan a method for her to use in trying to return to church. She stood first in the vestibule for a brief period and then returned home. The following Sunday she would remain longer. Through a gradual process she entered the back of the sanctuary and sat there for a part of the service. This pattern continued until she was finally able to remain for a complete church service. Although she usually had symptoms on entering

144

the church, she could not predict whether they would subside or get worse as the service of worship progressed. The celebration of Holy Communion was an especially trying time for her. Months passed before she was able to participate in this solemn religious rite. She stated that in this type of service God would not permit hypocrites participating.

After she was able to tolerate her symptoms in church and remain there, even though she felt she would faint, I asked her to try to faint at the point she felt she could tolerate her symptoms no longer. The reader will recognize this technique as Viktor Frankl's "paradoxical intention." In situations in which the patient would ordinarily be overwhelmed by a particular symptom, Frankl encouraged him to try to bring on this symptom and to see how severe he could make it. The patient often found that he was unsuccessful in bringing on the symptom. In the same way my patient was unable to make herself faint in church.

In trying to understand the chain of events psychologically and neurophysiologically, one must understand what she did when she became anxious in church. She was able to confirm the fact that as her anxiety mounted she breathed more and more rapidly. After prolonged rapid breathing, fainting seemed most imminent. Thus, the anxiety brought on hyperventilation and the expected neurophysiological response of fainting.

When she made an effort to faint, as I had encouraged her to do, she found herself relaxing her whole body and blocking out almost all stimuli. She reported spontaneously that as she relaxed she hardly breathed at all. Thus, without awareness, she restored the body to its proper equilibrium and thus aborted the fainting.

An important factor in this patient's treatment was her relationship with her wise and understanding pastor. She saw him occasionally during her long absence from church attendance and also when she began her efforts to return to church. According to the patient one of the most meaningful and helpful statements her pastor made to her was: "If you did not believe in God, you would not be worrying, for how could you be afraid of the God who did not exist." At this point I commended her for being concerned with her doubts and energetically working to understand them. Also I emphasized that the doubts were evidence of faith or else she would not be afraid of this God whom she had challenged to reveal himself.

She replied: "Then my doubts are a form of affirmation. I believe that with my heart but cannot with my head. Yet, I am aware all the time that even the great Christians of the past had their doubts and went through much religious questioning."

Her concept of God was that of the stern father who was all-seeing, all-knowing, and all-powerful. He kept a book in which was recorded each person's good and bad deeds. Judgment was more characteristic of him than love, mercy, or forgiveness. Although she frequently made no distinction between God and Christ, at times she did, as revealed in the following statement: "In my prayers I frequently ask Christ to take me in his arms. I want him to love and comfort me. I want to feel his presence so that I will get over this fear that I do not believe in the existence of God." Shortly thereafter she said, "I know God has his hands outstretched toward me, but I can't find my way to him."

As the patient began to recover, she reported in one session that she felt that God was going to forgive her. In this same session she began to realize how closely tied together were her religious and sexual concerns. Part of the session is reported verbatim:

Patient: Since you are trained both theologically and psychiatrically, answer a question for me theologically. Do you think God will forgive me?

Therapist: Yes. Your problem is born out of goodness—not badness. You require perfection on your part and will not permit yourself to doubt at times. Why do you ask if God will forgive you?

Patient: Because I tempted him to such an extent. It wasn't a small temptation. Of course, one sin is as big as another.

Therapist: Do you feel that you have committed a sin that cannot be pardoned?

Patient: Yes, definitely—the unpardonable sin. I have had this feeling for about a year, and it is related to my doubts about God. Actually after I felt I had committed it I still didn't know what the unpardonable sin was, except maybe a sin against the Holy Ghost.

Therapist: What do you understand the sin to be?

Patient: I don't exactly know. I had tempted him and lost my faith in him. The Holy Spirit gives you faith.

Therapist: The theologians don't know what the unpardonable sin is.

Patient: My pastor said the same thing and that he could neither define nor explain it. The day that I felt I had committed the unpardonable sin, I read in the newspaper a letter which had been written to Billy Graham. The writer of the letter had committed adultery and she was trying to find out if she had committed the unpardonable sin. So in my mind, I connected adultery with the unpardonable sin.

Therapist: Previously you connected the unpardonable sin with doubt and tempting God. Now you are connecting it with adultery. Had you noticed this before?

Patient: No. Billy Graham's reply to the woman was that she had not committed the unpardonable sin. And if she had committed adultery, she would be forgiven.

Therapist: How do you feel about Billy Graham's response to this letter?

Patient: I am not sure that there isn't a relationship between adultery and the unpardonable sin. Just the same, I have begun to feel better.

Therapist: In what way?

Patient: Last Sunday I began to feel that things will be all right. I feel now that I can go to church again. If I have a few doubts, I won't let them bother me. Also, if God strikes me dead, there is nothing I can do about it. I can now accept that possibility.

Therapist: I think that is a good approach to the problem.

Patient: I feel that we are put on this earth for a certain period of time. God is going to carry through his plan for me, rather than what I think.

The remainder of the session was spent discussing her husband. She mentioned how well they were now communicating

147

with each other. Also when she felt strong sexual stirrings she would reach out for him and enjoy the sexual experience. Previously she could not accept her sexual feelings but would suppress or hide them. Sex finally lost its dirty, disgusting features. She stated that after the sex act, in which she was almost always orgastic, she felt tranquil and free of guilt.

Meaning of Her Symptoms

Projective psychological testing of this patient confirmed the clinical findings. The test results presented a picture of a bright, normally intelligent individual who exhibited a panic-like state, manifested by an immobilization of goal-directed ideas, thoughts, and behavior. Obsessive rumination with ideas of a sexual nature permeated the findings. There was evidence to suggest that the patient characteristically prohibited the expression of any feelings and impulses inconsistent with an orientation to life which emphasized morality, orderliness, and organization. Internally and externally determined factors were focusing her attention upon sexual matters unacceptable to her. The resulting anxiety of panic proportions manifested itself through a generalized immobility of feeling and acting.

Preoccupation with sexual thoughts was inferred from the numerous Rorschach percepts of male and female genitalia given by the patient. An inferred inability to cope adequately with sexual matters could be made from many Rorschach percepts. Sexual thoughts and feelings were unacceptable to her and were seen as male and animal attributes.

An inability to resolve the apparent conflict between maintaining her moralistic, well-structured orientation to life and giving vent to her sexual feelings seemingly caused her to be fearful of her impulses and to become somewhat depressed. There was evidence of long-standing conflict over the unacceptability of the free expression of her instinctual life (sexual and hostile impulses), although this expression would be well within the limits of social acceptability.

From the material discussed in the therapy sessions with this patient, one readily sees that religion and sex were tied tightly together. She brought up much material which would suggest that God had failed her in helping her control her sexual thoughts. She was especially pained by her sexual thoughts in church. Her sexual fantasies in church, addressed to Christ, overwhelmed and immobilized her with panic. "Probably God did not exist, for he did not prevent my bad thoughts," seemed often to be implied by her.

During therapy the resolution of her religious problem took place at the same time that she accepted her sexuality. When she began to describe her ability to remain comfortable in church during a service of worship, she also spoke of the improved relationship with her husband and the pleasure she now enjoyed in this area.

The distinguished British psychoanalyst Augusta Bonnard states that most of the patients whom she has seen with church phobias can be grouped together as to psychodynamics:

For some people, religion lends itself to eroticisation. Such persons discover in their horror that not even in church are they safe from sensual thoughts or erotic sensations. Because of this, that is on a conscious level, they develop a fear of the place which they feel has failed to save them. On the other hand, of course, because of the omniscience of God they feel they are desecrating the church, knowing themselves to be the subject of erotic processes while in it. These awarenesses are then repressed in symptom formation.[1]

Summary

This thirty-seven-year-old white woman became phobic for church after she challenged God during a church service to prove his existence by striking her dead. After that, panic swept over her whenever she tried to attend church. About three years after her challenge to God she sought psychotherapy.

It soon became evident that the nucleus of her psychopathology was sexual conflict. Although she always had intense sexual needs, she denied or suppressed these. In church, painful and unacceptable sexual fantasies about Christ came to her

[1] Used by permission.

mind. God did not seem to protect her from these thoughts. In her desperation to get his help she presented him with an awful challenge.

Finally she was able partly to separate sex from religion. She worked through her feelings about sex and succeeded in establishing a very compatible relationship with her husband.

She was able to return to church and to worship meaningfully during the service. She was able to feel that God would not accept her challenge addressed to him. She began to realize that even though faith both conquers and encompasses doubt, it does not eradicate it, and that the person who denies doubt as a part of his faith is indeed a fanatic.

Although her basic character structure changed very little, she became free of symptoms, returned to a reasonably tranquil state, and functioned effectively in her home and community.

IV

TO HEAL AT TIMES
TO RELIEVE OFTEN
TO COMFORT ALWAYS

10

From Conflict to Cooperation
Between Religion and Psychiatry

The extent of suffering from mental illness is appalling, in our country and in the world. We face the dual challenge of what is our part in the healing of these sick people and what can be done to prevent mental illness. Many individuals and groups are interested. They represent a diversity of belief, training, and action. Two disciplines actively involved are psychiatry and religion. Representatives of these two groups have often been enemies; at other times only rivals; and, at present, they are often allies in a concerted effort to cure and prevent the psychic ills of men.

The physically ill person, no matter how far into history one probes, has seldom doubted that he was sick. In his pain he learned to ask others to help him relieve his physical distress. Out of the patient's request for help appeared the primitive doctor who tried to supply what the patient demanded. This effort has been the potent stimulus to advances in medicine and surgery through the ages. The patient has generally idealized his doctor and imposed upon him an ethical tradition which has undergone little modification through the centuries.

If one looks at mental illness, the picture of the historical process is different from that of physical illness. The mentally ill patient has not always been aware of illness or change within himself. And whereas he may have looked "different" to those around him, he was often considered spirit-possessed and endowed with special powers. He was indulged and revered, rather than treated. Medicine was denied the right to tamper with this supernatural being, and the sick one in turn seldom sought a doctor. This attitude delayed the introduction of medicine into the field of mental disease. Doctors, as products of their eras and cultures, did not attempt to violate the mores of their communities and left the care of the mentally ill in the hands of the priest. Thus, treatment ranged from the granting of special privileges to being burned at the stake.

During the Middle Ages mental illness was associated with witchcraft, and countless patients were executed in numerous ways by the church and the state. At this same time there were some quiet monasteries which cared for the deranged with kindness and humility.[1] But whichever treatment prevailed, the "spirit-possessed" person was for a long time denied medical treatment.

In the evolution of medical specialties psychiatry did not develop along the same lines as medicine and surgery. Zilboorg has described lucidly the opposition the physician encountered:

He faced danger to his reputation and person when he tried to convince the world that the "insane" were ill and to convert the neurotic and the "insane" to the singular belief that they were sick people and could be treated as such and cured. The patient suffering from appendicitis created the abdominal surgeon, the feverish and delirious man who had a sharp pain in his chest created the specialist in pneumonia, but it was the doctor who created the specialty of psychiatry. He did it uninvited and against terrible odds, against the will of the public, against the will of established legal authority, and against the will of a variety of established religious faiths.[2]

In addition to those of the medical profession, Zilboorg might have also mentioned many laymen and churchmen who have made major contributions in this field, and made them at times when their enlightened efforts met bitter opposition.

[1] Walter Bromberg, *Man Above Humanity: A History of Psychotherapy* (Philadelphia: J. B. Lippincott, 1954), pp. 38-42.
[2] Gregory Zilboorg, *A History of Medical Psychology* (New York: W. W. Norton and Co., 1941), pp. 21-26.

Medicine, as a newcomer in the treatment of mental disease, has had to force its way into this field. For centuries jurisprudence, theology, and philosophy have dealt with the insane, and even today are reluctant to relinquish their right of eminent domain. In the light of this historical perspective the present-day relationships of psychiatry with these related disciplines are more easily understood.

The intrusion of psychiatry was perhaps most strongly felt by the theologians whose feelings of distrust of this specialty were enhanced by the atheistic bias of the early psychiatrists. Freud and his colleagues were heirs of a curious double legacy from the eighteenth and nineteenth centuries. These psychiatrists were, philosophically speaking, descendents of the eighteenth-century Enlightenment, that great movement of religious humanism. The emphasis was not on a City of God in heaven but on a heavenly city of man on earth, wherein a good society was achieved for men and by men, ordered by reason and experience. Although the Enlightenment was not irreligious, its belief in the capacity of man to control his conditions in life was to a great extent anti-Christian.

The other great ideological force which molded the general atheism of Freud and his followers was the reductive naturalism of the nineteenth century. Human values emerge in a natural process that is otherwise blind or indifferent to the human enterprise. Man makes of nature what he can, and it is a foolish illusion to believe that nature is the created organism in which God is working out his purpose.

These two traditions of religious humanism and reductive naturalism came into sharp conflict with the Judeo-Christian tradition. Although Freud denied any interest in the question of philosophical presuppositions, powerful residues of these movements are evident in his system-building and constructs. One can also observe this influence when exploring the attitudes of psychiatrists toward personality, freedom, philosophy, ethics, and religion.

Another factor influencing Freud's philosophy of life, and especially his attitude toward religion, was the religious life of

Vienna in his day. He was a Jew, encircled and influenced by the obsessively anti-Semitic culture of Imperial Austria. It is unfortunate that Freud, living in the Vienna and Europe of 1875 to 1925, came into contact with poor manifestations of religious faith. He could find nothing challenging in his own Jewish faith in Vienna, in the Roman Catholicism of the Austrian Empire, or in the Protestantism of Victorian England. His conclusions about religion arose in part from unhappy experiences with followers of the three great faiths. Also the use and misuse of religion by his patients gave him a distorted view of religion.

A fresh religious breeze which swept across Germany during the latter part of the nineteenth and early part of the twentieth centuries was the movement of higher criticism, followed during and after World War I by the movement of form criticism (*formgeschichte*).[3] This new direction in biblical research, of which Albert Schweitzer was a part, scrutinized and criticized the origins and development of the biblical writings, bringing to bear every tool of scientific investigation available and appropriate. The scholars involved in this school were kindred spirits in some ways with Freud, yet he seems to have had no awareness of their existence and their creative search for truth in biblical research and exegesis. Possibly a solid acquaintance with these scholars would have softened his pessimism about the church.

Karl Stern, a prominent Canadian psychiatrist, has often said that Freud's atheistic philosophy is a tragic accident of history.[4] This atheistic philosophy so blinded churchmen that they could not see the monumental contribution Freud had made through the theory, insights, and techniques of psychoanalysis. The church delayed for a half-century before appropriating and utilizing the psychoanalytic insights so desperately needed in its work of education, training, and counseling.

Many have tried to deemphasize Freud's attacks on religion.

---

[3] E. B. Redlich, *Form Criticism* (London: Duckworth Press, 1939).
[4] *The Pillar of Fire* (New York: Harcourt, Brace and Co., 1939).

This is unrealistic when the record is studied. Religion was a continually recurring topic in his writings during the entire course of his long and productive life. His earliest attack upon religion is to be found in an article entitled "Obsessive Acts and Religious Practices," published in 1907 and now available in Volume II of his *Collected Papers*. In this paper he stressed the similarity between religious expressions of piety and the obsessive behavior of his neurotic patients. He reiterated and expanded this theme in a series of four volumes which followed: *Totem and Tabu*, 1913; *The Future of an Illusion*, 1928; *Civilization and Its Discontents*, 1930; and *Moses and Monotheism*, 1939.

When one examines Freud's antireligious bias, he sees also the "other side of the coin." Freud had to be interested in religion to spend so much time talking and writing about it. He gave more published attention to religion than to any other subject except the theory and practice of psychoanalysis as a form of therapy. Some argue that he was close to some kind of personal acceptance of religion[5] in spite of the fact that Freud denied this in his *New Introductory Lectures*, in 1933. He felt that religious influence arrested man's growing understanding of the universe and of himself, and it was necessary that Freud give serious attention to this powerful enemy.

In spite of his attacks on organized religion and his rejection of any kind of personal religious commitment, his debt to one religious tradition as a source of many of his psychoanalytic ideas is brilliantly discussed by David Bakan.[6] Bakan's hypothesis is that a full appreciation of the development of psychoanalysis is essentially incomplete unless it be viewed against the history of Judaism, and particularly against the history of Jewish mystical thought. Freud, as a Jew, says Bakan, had learned to think in the traditionally Jewish mystical manner; and any person brought up in a Jewish environment will inevi-

[5] Gregory Zilboorg, "Some Denials and Affirmations of Religious Faith," in *Faith, Reason and Modern Psychiatry*, ed. F. J. Braceland (New York: P. J. Kenedy and Sons, 1955), p. 99.

[6] *Freud and the Jewish Mystical Tradition* (Princeton, N.J.: D. Van Nostrand, 1958).

tably absorb something of this mode of thinking, to remain with him all the years of his life. Bakan goes on to show that the Jewish mystical tradition is essentially Kabbalistic, using the term in a general sense to mean not only the traditional, but also to cover most of those works, which, like the Zohar, were designed to show the newly initiated how to extract the hidden meanings and mysteries from the scriptures. Secrecy, power, and mystery pervade the Kabbalistic tradition. Bakan argues that Freud, in his thinking, is in the direct line of succession to the Kabbalists. He compares the Kabbalistic tradition with certain aspects of psychoanalysis: "The Kabbalistic tradition has it that the secret teachings are to be transmitted orally to one person at a time, and even then only to selected minds and by hints. This is indeed what Freud was doing in the actual practice of psychoanalysis, and this aspect of the Kabbalistic tradition is still maintained in the education of the modern psychoanalyst. He must receive the tradition orally (in the training analysis). As the modern practicing psychoanalyst is quick to tell anyone, psychoanalysis is not to be learned from books!" [7]

Much of what Freud described and attacked as religion deserved his criticism. The sterility of the established churches of his time has already been described. Later some qualms appeared to strike him because of his wholesale condemnation. He admitted that he must bow to the reproach that he had no consolation to offer humanity.[8]

He had many close religious friends. Chief among them was Oskar Pfister, Swiss clergyman and psychoanalyst. Dr. Pfister joined Freud for training when the psychoanalytic movement was in its infancy. He enjoyed throughout the years Freud's lasting friendship and confidence. Dr. Pfister functioned in the dual capacity of clergyman and psychoanalyst. He wrote widely and probably made his greatest contribution in the application of psychoanalytic insights to the field of education. Several of Freud's letters to him are available and contain some revealing

[7] Sigmund Freud, "On the History of the Psychoanalytic Movement," *Collected Papers*, I, 35-36.
[8] Freud, *Civilization and Its Discontents*, p. 143.

and illuminating information.[9] In a letter to Pfister, dated February 9, 1909, he reveals a very positive feeling about the work of the pastor:

You . . . have young people with recent conflicts who are attached to you personally, and who are in a suitable state for sublimation and, indeed, for its most convenient form—religious sublimation . . . . You are in the fortunate position of leading them on to God and reconstructing the conditions of earlier times, fortunate at least in the one respect that religious piety stifles neuroses . . . . In itself psychoanalysis is neither religious nor the opposite, but an impartial instrument which can serve the clergy as well as the laity when it is used only to free suffering people. I have been very struck at realizing how I had never thought of the extraordinary help the psychoanalytic method can be in pastoral work, probably because wicked heretics like us are so far away from that circle." [10]

August Aichhorn, an educator and worker with juvenile delinquents,[11] was also a close friend of Freud. Although he did not profess allegiance to a particular religious persuasion, his treatment techniques in his school for delinquents were based on New Testament principles. This is strongly emphasized in Oskar Pfister's essay on Aichhorn, published in the book, *Searchlights on Delinquency*.[12]

Another close friend of Freud who was devoutly religious was the distinguished James J. Putnam, professor of neuropathology at Harvard. Freud came to America in 1909 to present a series of lectures to a group celebrating the twentieth anniversary of Clark University at Worcester, Massachusetts. During this visit the friendship between Freud and Putnam developed. Putnam was convinced that Freud's discoveries confirmed and extended

[9] A recently published book contains a great deal of this correspondence: *Psychoanalysis and Faith, The Letters of Sigmund Freud and Oskar Pfister* (New York: Basic Books, 1963).

[10] Ernest Jones, *The Life and Work of Sigmund Freud* (New York: Basic Books, 1955), II, 439-40.

[11] Aichhorn describes his experiences in his book *Wayward Youth* (New York: Viking, 1953).

[12] Oskar Pfister, "Therapy and Ethics in August Aichhorn's Treatment of Wayward Youth," in *Searchlights on Delinquency*, ed. K. R. Eissler (New York: International Universities Press, 1949).

many of his own psychiatric ideas. He became an effective representative of the psychoanalytic movement in America. Freud graciously acknowledged his indebtedness to this man of lofty ethical standards and moral rectitude in tributes such as this one: "The esteem he enjoyed throughout America on account of his high moral character and unflinching love of truth was of great service to psychoanalysis and protected it against the denunciations which might otherwise have early overwhelmed it." [13]

It is interesting to note that Putnam felt that the psychoanalytic theories required a wider philosophical and ethical orientation than Freud had allowed. He insisted to Freud, Ernest Jones, and others that psychoanalysis as a science should be linked to a particular philosophical system, and that its clinical practice should be openly associated with a particular set of ethical doctrines. Freud seemed to interpret this solicitude of Putnam as a natural outgrowth of Putnam's religious concerns and his desire to establish the closest relations between psychoanalysis and the aims which lay nearest his heart. Freud and his followers, however, rejected Putnam's proposals. In the preface to Putnam's posthumous *Addresses on Psycho-Analysis*, Freud explained that he and his colleagues rejected Putnam's proposals because of their doubt as to which of the countless philosophical systems should be accepted.[14] The theologian Albert C. Outler states that Freud and his associates rejected Putnam's proposals because they already had a philosophical system, that of humanism and reductive naturalism.[15]

Although one may be offended by Freud's amateur theology and his atheistic, deterministic philosophy, it should be remembered that his philosophic views are totally separate from his psychoanalytic theories and techniques. If he had only developed psychoanalysis and said or written nothing about his atheistic philosophy, he would have been far more widely ac-

[13] "On the History of the Psychoanalytic Movement," in *Collected Papers*, I, 315.

[14] (New York: International Psycho-Analytical Press, 1921).

[15] *Psychotherapy and the Christian Message* (New York: Harper & Bros., 1954), p. 60.

cepted today by the church. Many churchmen are so blinded by his religious views that they cannot look further to see his monumental contributions toward the understanding of human behavior.

In spite of the atheistic viewpoint of the early psychoanalytic movement, much is happening today in a cooperative way between psychiatry and religion.

Carl Gustav Jung should be given recognition for his contribution. His religious attitudes were the first antidote within psychiatry to those of Freud. Freud stressed an analysis of the patient's past in psychotherapy. Jung tended to stress the present life situation and an overall need for a synthesis on the part of an individual. He recognized one of the psychological values of religion as providing an individual's life with unity and meaning. Religion, thus, played a more important role in the therapeutic methods of Jung than in those of Freud. Many Roman Catholic writers, such as Victor White, Louis Beiernaert, Karl Stern, and Gerald Vann, have shown themselves to be in considerable agreement with the Jungian theories of the collective unconscious, of archetypal symbols, and of the innate religious function. On the other hand, there has probably been a closer correspondence between the Protestant tradition and Freudianism. Especially in America, more attention has been given to Freud than Jung by Protestant churchmen. Protestantism has not had the confessional, and possibly this has been one of the reasons why it developed a strong pastoral counseling ministry earlier than Roman Catholicism. Also, the general Protestant approach, regarding techniques and insights, is likely to have more in common with Freudian analysis than Jungian psychology.[16]

Pope Pius XII performed a much-needed task of clarification in reference to the Roman Catholic attitude toward psychiatry. On April 13, 1953, he spoke to the Fifth International Congress on Psychotherapy and Clinical Psychology in an address entitled "On Psychotherapy and Religion." [17] This was the first papal

---

[16] F. W. Dillistone, "The Christian Doctrine of Man and Modern Psychological Theories," *The Hibbett Journal*, LIV (1959), 157-60.

[17] (Washington: National Catholic Welfare Conference, 1953).

document dealing formally with the question of psychiatry, and it was heartening and forward-looking. He encouraged Roman Catholics to "labor on a terrain that is very difficult," and assured them that their activity in this area was "capable of achieving precious results for medicine, for the knowledge of the soul in general, for the religious dispositions of man and for their development."

In the past ten years there has been consistent encouragement from both psychiatry and religion for a unified outlook toward the mental health problems of our age.

The oldest and one of the most successful forms of collaboration is through the mental-hospital chaplain. The chaplain's training generally represents a joint effort of psychiatrists and clergymen. This work is coordinated through the Council for Clinical Training.

Important psychiatric centers, such as the Menninger Foundation, have been active in many cooperative efforts between religion and psychiatry. Many training centers have been established like that of the Institute of Religion, Houston, Texas. Theological seminaries are developing programs in psychiatry and religion which offer instruction in basic psychiatric knowledge, psychodynamics, pastoral counseling, etc. Also, some significant dialogue is taking place between theologians and psychiatrists, and efforts are being made to develop a psychiatry for theology as well as a theology for psychiatry.

An achievement with great potential for cooperative endeavor began with the establishment of the Academy of Religion and Mental Health in 1955. The Academy brings together psychiatrists and clergymen of all faiths and members of other related disciplines, for consideration and resolution of problems arising between religion and psychiatry, and for work together as a multidisciplinary approach in many areas of mental health and illness. Its growth and accomplishments have been phenomenally great.

In conclusion, a note of warning should be sounded about one aspect of the cooperative efforts of psychiatry and religion. Some clergymen, trained in pastoral counseling and the hospital chaplaincy, look upon themselves only as psychotherapists and gradually abandon the priestly role. They establish private offices, do psychotherapy, charge fees, and are responsible to no authority for the caliber of their performance or ethics of their conduct. The very term "pastoral counselor" implies that a pastorate should be involved. And, when a pastorate is involved, the clergyman is responsible to his congregation and to higher ecclesiastical authorities. A psychotherapist responsible to no authorized authority is a far cry from the psychiatrist who must answer to his state board of medical examiners, his county medical society, and the courts of law in medicolegal responsibility. Psychiatry's major contribution to the clergyman's training is to impart to him its knowledge of human behavior in order that he, as a pastor, may use psychiatric insights in his pastoral and priestly functions—in crises such as illness and death, in preaching, in premarital counseling, in religious education programs, and in pastoral counseling. Most psychiatrists consider it a special opportunity to aid in the training of the pastor, but not to aid him in becoming a private psychotherapist, who, to some extent, may be lost to the life and work of the church. The church has nurtured, through the years, the pastoral counseling movement. Now that some clergymen in this movement are withdrawing from a formal relationship with the church and are forming or affiliating with private psychotherapy clinics, the church is losing one of its rich resources. I hope the church will be successful in holding within its structure the pastoral counseling movement. The pastoral counselor with a firm commitment to the church and a clear identity as to his role does speak with the authority of God and the church. This authority which he possesses adds an important dimension to his counseling and is the unique attribute of genuine pastoral counseling which is done within the framework of the church.

It is encouraging that psychiatry and religion are joining hands in many cooperative efforts. Many of their goals are similar. Each needs the other if individuals are to be ministered to as total persons.

11

Partners in Healing:
The Pastor, the Patient
and the Physician

In a recent issue of *The Lutheran* Reuben K. Youngdahl writes: "In East Africa a group of natives, having made a long journey seeking medical care, walked right past a government hospital to reach a mission hospital. When asked why they had walked the extra distance, when the government hospital had exactly the same medicine, they replied, 'The medicine may be the same, but the hands are different.' " [1] In that extra ingredient, symbolized by the hands that are different, may be found an understanding of healing which colors the concept of modern scientific medicine. In the mission hospital medicine and the ministry were unified into one vocation, one service.

The Meaning of Illness or Disease

Any discussion of disease involves not only medicine but philosophy and religion, as well as the social and behavioral sciences. Man is a product of his total environment, and disease is a protest of the whole man. Disease is more than a matter of invading germs or hardening of the arteries, for more universal factors play an immense role in the production of disease. The division of medicine into specialties and subspecialties has given us detailed knowledge of the superficial and obvious mechanisms of certain diseases but has delayed our realization of the deeper factors which underlie all disease.

A recent article by Harold G. Wolff reports data from a variety of studies to indicate that it is unprofitable to establish a

[1] "Throughway Love," *The Lutheran*, December 4, 1963.

164

separate category of illness defined as psychosomatic or to separate sharply the genesis of psychiatric, medical, and surgical disease.[2] Wolff suggests a unified concept of disease related to the outcome of attempts at adaptation. Man's attempts at adaptation are made not only to damaging microbial, mechanical, and chemical forces, but even as importantly to threats and symbols of danger, particularly as they involve his relations with other people. Under circumstances perceived as threatening, behavioral and attitudinal reactions serving to protect in a crisis may become inappropriate in amount and kind, according to Wolff. When inappropriate in kind, they may block proper interaction and communication with other people and distort circumstances so as to prevent an appropriate response. Also evoked may be primitive physiological patterns ordinarily serving to maintain the body but now inappropriate to the stimulus in kind as well as in amount. These patterns may be called upon to achieve ends that they never can attain and the resulting inappropriate reactions may be protracted for an indefinite length of time. Functions which are usually phasic become continuous. Thus the tissues involved are pressed beyond their limits. In certain instances this leads promptly to dysfunction, to symptoms, and to evidences of disease. In other cases it manifests itself by acceleration of the processes of aging, and bodily diseases commonly found in man's later decades are then found to occur in the fourth and fifth decades and may result in death prematurely.

In the early twentieth century it became widely accepted that stressful life circumstances, including interpersonal relationships, could be major factors in disease. Disorders designated as "psychosomatic diseases," as well as psychoneuroses and psychoses, were singled out as illnesses where this relationhip was most evident. Now, in the second half of the century, it becomes increasingly evident that such periods of stress may have for man sweeping implications for illnesses of all kinds.

[2] "A Concept of Disease in Man," *Psychosomatic Medicine*, XXIV (January-February, 1962).

Since man is a tribal creature with a long period of development, he depends for his very existence on the aid, support, comfort, and encouragement of those about him. His interactions with other men are so close that he is deeply concerned about their expectations of him. Perhaps his greatest threat is their disapproval and rejection. He also needs to develop himself in the way he personally feels that he should, and to be himself. During periods of rapid social change, men may feel so threatened as to resolve their conflicts by totally subordinating their own proclivities and fulfillments to the common end or to the glory of their group. When his efforts are frustrated, when he is separated from or rejected by his group, the individual may seriously abreact or even die.

In studying any illness one should always ask: (1) What does this illness mean for the individual in whom the signs and symptoms of disease reside? What is he telling us about his emotional and spiritual condition? (2) What does this illness tell us about the family from which the sick individual comes? (3) What does this illness tell us about the community from which the sick individual comes? (4) What changes should take place in the individual, the family, and the community to help the patient regain and maintain his health?

Sigmund Freud's main thesis is that mental illness is a meaningful phenomenon, that its language can be understood and, therefore, should be listened to. For years Anton Boisen has proclaimed that although mental illnesses in many cases represent adaptations to defeat and failure which have been made and accepted, there are other forms of mental illness which, like fever and inflammation, are manifestations of the body's healing power.[3] Gotthard Booth[4], Lawrence LeShan[5], Aarne Siirala[6], among many others, have written of the meaningful language of the body and have urged the individual, in the situation of men-

[3] "Religious Experience and Psychological Conflict," *Pastoral Psychology*, XII (1961), 15-18.
[4] "Disease as a Message," *Journal of Religion and Health*, I (1962), 309-18.
[5] "A Basic Psychological Orientation Apparently Associated with Malignant Disease," *The Psychiatric Quarterly*, April, 1961.
[6] "The Meaning of Illness," *Journal of Religion and Health*, I (1962), 153-64.

tal or physical illness, to listen to what his body is trying to say through its illness.

There is a renewed interest today in the relationship of separation, of real or fantasied loss, as a contributing factor to acute and chronic illness, of both a physical and psychological nature. We are familiar with such expressions as "he died of a broken heart"; "he just gave in to being sick"; "there was nothing to live for." Such statements are made to explain a change in the health of an individual following his loss of a loved one. Such ideas come from many sources, including personal experiences, folklore, literature, drama, and religious teachings. In medical practice during the eighteenth and nineteenth centuries it was common to ascribe illness to grief, bereavement, disappointment, despair, and mental depression. At other times illness has been explained as a punishment for sins. With the development of scientific medicine interest in the pathophysiology of disease took precedence over psychological and spiritual factors. Physicians and their patients thought people died not of grief and despair but of heart disease, cancer, and other clear-cut organic diseases. Recently investigations have reawakened interest in the psychological settings in which illness develops.

Reports of the disease and death-producing effects of ostracism are widely known and accepted.[7] The phenomenon of separation and loss as a contributing factor to illness is exemplified well by certain prisoners of war. Some felt they were in impossible or insoluble situations[8] and gave up. Others became ill and died without apparent reason.[9]

While the sense of apartness was often identified in the past as the most important factor common to both psychological and spiritual malaise, now, through research on separation and loss, the illnesses once associated with apartness can be extended to include also certain organic illnesses. Reports in the medical

[7] W. B. Cannon, "Voodoo Death," *American Anthropology*, XLIV (1942), 169.
[8] H. D. Strassman, et. al., "A Prisoner of War Syndrome—Apathy as a Reaction to Severe Stress," *American Journal of Psychiatry*, CXII (1956), 998.
[9] J. Tas, "Psychical Disorders Among Inmates of Concentration Camps," *Psychiatric Quarterly*, XXV (1951), 679.

literature have singled out real or threatened loss as a precipitating factor in the development of a variety of disorders which include cancer, thyrotoxicosis, asthma, tuberculosis, ulcerative colitis, obesity, leukemia, and lymphoma, rheumatoid arthritis, congestive heart failure, disseminated lupus erythematosus, Raynaud's disease, diabetes mellitus, infectious hepatitis, and functional uterine bleeding. Our present knowledge of disease makes us cautious about identifying any one factor as the cause of an illness. It is better to speak of a constellation of factors that enter into the development of a particular illness, with each factor perhaps weighted differently.

The importance of emotional factors, such as separation and loss, along with physical factors, must all be considered. For example, in an asthmatic attack the emotional component may be present as a precipitating factor, but other factors probably playing a part may be exposure to allergenic substances, an infection, fatigue, change in temperature, etc. The importance of each factor will vary with each individual and with each disease process.

The meaning of the illness for the family from which the patient comes also deserves our attention. This should be given searching scrutiny, for a family can choose one member to be sick, to be the scapegoat. European psychiatrists and clergymen have emphasized this more than we have in this country. While conducting a research project in a South American city I discovered that some families spoke of the mentally ill one in their family as the "dark one." Thus the sick one tells us something of the sickness of the family and the soil out of which illness has grown. Recently while a child was being evaluated, he told the psychiatrist, "I have to be sick in order to save my family."

The illnesses of individuals tell us a great deal about the communities in which these individuals live. This is easy to accept when we speak of drug addictions, alcoholism, juvenile delinquency, and crime. However, we must extend this list to include mental and physical illnesses. Do any or all of these illnesses tell us anything about the prevailing value system in the community, the structure of the social institutions, or the philosophical and religious life of the community? These illnesses speak to the community, and the individual most readily finds healing when his community is healed also.

The Priestly Function in Healing

The body's capacity to renew itself, its unwillingness to accept defeat and death, has already been discussed in the chapter entitled "The Body's Miraculous Wisdom." The natural recuperative powers of the body can be assisted to work more effectively by a physician or by a clergyman. There was a time in our history when the medical and priestly roles were combined in the priest-doctor. Certain aspects of this tradition exist today. The term "father-confessor" is used not infrequently by patients to describe the functions of the doctor to whom they confide their troubles. The successful doctor is almost always a father figure. The British psychiatrist Arthur Guirdham warns us in *Christ and Freud:* "One of the most certain guarantees of the future decline of medicine is the fact that you cannot make a father-figure from a subordinate official of the civil service." [10] Guirdham goes on to say that perhaps the best the patient can do is to regard the civil service physician as a diluted version of Big Brother. I can appreciate Guirdham's warning, but I have seen many young interns, serving on the staffs of city hospitals, function splendidly as father figures. Guirdham is rightly emphasizing, however, the danger in trying to make the services of those in the healing role a commodity that is traded in the marketplace or a political football kicked around by those in politics.

Certain trends in society and in the medical profession minimize the concept of the doctor as healer, that is, endowed with intrinsic powers of healing. Some individuals believe that the modern physician is essentially a vehicle for the application of certain scientific principles. We seem to be moving toward the view that one doctor is no different from another; that the pattern of treatment can be laid down in directives issued by a

[10] (New York: Collier Books, 1962).

governmental agency; and that the disease response of an individual who likes Bach's fugues is the same as one who likes only rock 'n' roll music. The concept of the physician as a healer, one whose hands make the difference, cannot flourish in the atmosphere of materialism which stifles present-day medicine.

In a superficial sense one can say that in pneumonia, penicillin will be equally effective whatever doctor injects the medication. To a great extent this is true. Yet, even in the infectious diseases, there are multiple factors operating in healing. The diseases related to life's stresses are usually more complicated in their development and treatment than are the infectious diseases. Still, one cannot exclude the role played by life's stresses in infectious diseases, such as colds, tuberculosis, etc. The response of the patient in the treatment of disease is not independent of the nature of the doctor (his own essence). It is widely known in the treatment of many functional illnesses that the outlook depends greatly on the nature, as distinct from the capacities, of the first doctor who handles them. Often the most successful physicians are the most silent, for their effect on their patients depends less on their words than on themselves. The physicians who lecture to their patients frankly as to the nature of their symptoms are not necessarily successful. Much depends on whether the doctor exerts positive or negative suggestion. He may be a reassuring remover of symptoms or a lugubrious inducer of them. However, apart from suggestion, the physician can, knowingly or unknowingly, bring healing to the patient or retard the course of healing.

Today, physicians seem much more proud of the term "science of medicine" than they are of the "art of medicine," yet the oldest term for the practice of medicine was the "healing art." There should be no need to minimize the importance of intrinsic healing attributes in those who practice the art of medicine. John P. McGovern, pediatrician and allergist, of Baylor University College of Medicine, suggests the term the "science of the art of medicine." Such a term indicates the blending of the highest scientific skills with the use of the physician himself as an instrument of therapy. Dr. McGovern has given us a term which we should take seriously, for it suggests a synthesis needed today in medicine. A fusion of the healer and the scientist gives society the kind of doctor it needs.

Although modern medicine has made astounding progress in the treatment of infectious diseases during the past few decades, the total morbidity to which we are subject remains about the same. It is evident from an examination of national mortality statistics of recent decades that a degree of success has been achieved in postponing death. The incidence in Western civilization of psychosomatic and other stress diseases, as well as cancer and psychiatric illnesses, is probably rising. What kind of doctor will be able to treat successfully this group of noninfectious diseases? Guirdham suggests:

For the relief of the chronic disorders from which we suffer we need another kind of doctor. For the making of new men, new doctors are required. Should the latter ever appear, they will resemble neither doctors of the present vintage nor of any other in the course of modern European civilization. If the stress diseases are to be controlled, we must return to the conception of the wise man. The latter must have the knowledge and training of the doctor without his materialism, and the basic attributes of the priest without the paraphernalia of clericalism. He will also need the wisdom of the sage." [11]

If we take seriously Guirdham's statement, then we cannot accept such processes as spiritual, faith, or medical healing but only the total synchronizing process of healing. The goal is wholeness and harmony, for freedom from disease and health itself are fragmentary conceptions.

The Church's Ministry of Healing

In the Gospels of the New Testament one finds more attention devoted to the healing ministry of Jesus than any other subject except the passion story of the last week of Jesus' earthly life. One may ponder how the art and practice of healing, cen-

[11] Arthur Guirdham, *Cosmic Factors in Disease* (London: Duckworth & Co., 1963).

tral to the biblical record, has managed until recent time to become peripheral to theological education and to the central concerns of the organized church. Jesus trained his disciples in certain forms and methods of the healing art such as fasting, anointing with oil, laying on of hands, exorcism of demons, and the prayer of faith.

In studying the biblical healing stories one discovers several basic conditions operative in almost all of the cases described. An examination of these will show the similarity existing between ancient and modern healing, and furnish some guidelines for a healing ministry.

First, the healing takes place through the activity of an individual or group who are perceived as having the authority and power to heal. In most cases both the healer and the one being healed shared this conviction as to the authority and power of the healer. In those cases in which the one being healed is skeptical or agnostic there are significant other persons in his environment who do credit the healing person or persons with authority and power.

Second, the act of healing often includes the recital of previous healings or other divine events that manifest power for wholeness and transformation. Mircea Eliade, in *The Sacred and the Profane*, emphasizes that primitive man, in his healing rites, sought healing through the regeneration of the sources of his life with which he made contact through the ritual recitation of the story of creation. The sick man symbolically became contemporary with the "creation" and became well because he began life over again with his reserve of vital forces intact, as it was at the moment of his birth. Healings in the early church were done in the name of Jesus who was worshiped as the new creation, the second Adam. Jesus' conversation with Nicodemus about the second birth of the spirit (John 3:1-8), and the sacramental healing power ascribed to the action of baptism and the Eucharist, are examples of the theme of return to some primordial state from which a new creation may emerge.

Third, in the New Testament healing stories the healing action came in response to the initiative and request of the sick person, his friends, or his relatives. Active desire and expectancy permeated the healing situation. By the pool of Bethesda, before the healing took place, Jesus asked the man if he truly wanted to be healed (John 5:1-16).

Leslie Weatherhead maintains that a fundamental element in all the healing stories is the quality of "expectant trust." Jerome Frank, in *Persuasion and Healing*, shows expectant trust to be the central thread woven through all the healing practices of man, both ancient and modern. The many occasions on which Jesus states that the faith or expectancy of the sick person had been the fundamental instrumentality of the healing does serve to underline how absolutely essential this element seems to have been for the healings of the New Testament and the early church.

Fourth, healing seems to have taken place almost invariably in some corporate context. Jesus in his ministry was almost always surrounded by crowds of people. An example of this is the story of the sick man who had to be let down through the roof into the room where Jesus was because the door was blocked by large numbers of people (Mark 2:1-5). This story is especially significant because it appears to have been the friends and not the patient himself who sought the healing and had the expectant trust. The group atmosphere in the New Testament healing episodes was a most significant factor in the preparation and support of the healing process. In the life of the early church, where healing became more and more associated with the corporate worship and the sacramental life of the believing community, the element of group atmosphere became a factor of major importance.

The implications of this for the pastor and the present-day church are obvious. A neglected area of church activity is the use of the congregation as an instrument of therapy. The church as a therapeutic and redemptive community can have profound influence upon the health of the individual and the group. To give details of how the congregation could function in a variety of healing capacities is beyond the scope of this chapter. Consider what a great force the congregation would be if it functioned always with the devotion and dedication of Alcoholics Anonymous, for the group life in this organization is similar to the group life which the church could furnish to many people with a variety of problems and illnesses.

Fifth, in many of the instances of biblical healing the healer employs suggestion and authoritative verbal direction as an important part of his method. Jesus used this approach. Often this suggestive element was simply the communication of the firm assumption that the ill person would be healed of the illness.

Sixth, in many of the biblical stories physical materials and means were used as an instrumental aspect of the healing action. These included saliva for the stammering tongue, clay for the eyes, the laying on of hands, the anointing with oil, or the symbolic cleansing with water—all used to effect healing.

In the early church the Eucharist, anointing with oil, and baptism were the three major occasions of healing, according to Origen and others.

Religious healing of the type described here largely disappeared from the life of the church toward the end of the third century. Following Constantine, when the church became officially accepted, the healing ministry became extinct except in a few isolated communities. It continued to receive some attention within the monastic movement during the next ten centuries and broke out into popular awareness during periods of religious resurgence such as the Franciscan movement, the Reformation, the Wesleyan revival, and the current movements of church renewal in our time.

The church today is renewing its interest in the ministry of healing and making a serious effort to recapture the power of the early church. The pastor and his congregation, using the rich resources available to them through the church, can participate in a healing ministry desperately needed by modern man.

The Patient's Part in Healing

What, then, can we say today to the sick patient? For healing to take place medical knowledge and all that faith includes are needed. A combination must be made of what the doctor and the minister have to offer separately. It may be that the patient will have to do the synchronizing if health is to be achieved, when the doctor-priest is not available. In any event the patient has a major responsibility for attaining within himself such a state of balance that the natural forces of healing and renewal can predominate whether or not he is fortunate enough to have the guidance of a doctor-priest.

In order to see the scope and implications of this responsibility let us review some of the familiar words in our religious vocabulary: sin, repentance, sacrifice, atonement, love. Hopefully, theologians will permit us some freedom in assigning to the definition of these words a kind of existential component which will help us to clarify our religious course of action when faced with illness. Sin can be seen as estrangement from God and one's basic self or destiny. Repentance involves not only a change of mind but a change of behavior. The phase of it in which we are most interested is that of rethinking one's life, one's acts, one's goals. Atonement (at-one-ment) suggests the unifying of one's life and goals in conformity with God's will, becoming at one with God and his design for one's life. Sacrifice represents a reorganization of life which must be undertaken in order to achieve atonement. As insight is obtained through spiritual search and repentance, and is acted upon, however sacrificial this may appear to be, the weight of estrangement lifts and the balance is shifted in favor of health. The possibility of one's life being genuinely devoted to love and service increases as at-one-ment is approached. The basis for our need to love springs from our need to overcome the anxiety of separateness and to achieve union. This is so in our love of God, as well as man.

When illness is seen as deeply influenced by spiritual and emotional conditions, by separation from loved objects, by real or fantasied loss, by a lack of meaning in life, or by a sense of guilt, certain possibilities for health open up. This is not to say that illness should be treated only on the spiritual and emotional level. A sick person should attempt to obtain and conscientiously follow the best available medical regimen of treatment, whether it be in the form of medication, recommended change in living habits, operative procedures, psychotherapy, or the like. And herein lies one of the pitfalls. It is very easy to become so involved in following a physical regimen or in remembering to report one's dreams that the world closes in around the sick person. The sense of separation, lack of active participation in life, and the loss of friends may be brought on in greater severity by remaining absorbed in an illness beyond its most acute phase.

Contact with the sustaining life of others should be deliberately maintained through letters, telephone calls, graciously encouraging visitors, etc. This contact should not be primarily to share one's illness, although it certainly need not be a completely forbidden topic of conversation. The object should be to maintain an interested and helping role toward those one loves, to give and receive loving concern.

That leads to another pitfall—the danger of hypocrisy. There is doubtful benefit to be gained by appearing to be concerned for others unless this is really felt. Illness often temporarily cuts off one's feeling of love, and, for a certain length of time, repentance can be so absorbing that there is no possibility for outgoing emotions. Rather than making a sham of love when it is not felt, one may carefully cultivate the slightest stirrings of interest so that love is renewed.

In exploring the meaning of one's illness, perhaps the core problem is to repent, in the sense of rethinking one's way of life and goals and of clarifying what it is that gives life its meaning. Perhaps most often this is found in terms of certain persons, but it may be that dedication to certain aspects of creative production or work is central. Such was the situation with the young mother who had tuberculosis. She wondered why she should get well. Her decision to live for her daughter gave the meaning to her life for which she was searching. Meaning may have to be phrased in terms of what is worth dying for. Perhaps one must be ready to give one's life for meaning to be found.

The other side of the coin of repentance concerns the identifying of elements that are wasting life. Sometimes it becomes essential to identify what elements of life are unrewarding or which are filled with dread. It will be necessary in some way to rid life of the elements that are bearing bitter fruit. This may be a sacrifice. It may mean giving up something to which a great deal of time and effort have been devoted without reward. It is often difficult to admit that in our choice of a way of life, a marriage partner, a certain vocation, or in moral decisions we have been wrong. Or we may have to decide that we were not wrong, only lazy, stubborn, or misguided and that proper application of ourselves would straighten out a disturbing and sickening situation.

Those for whom life has become so barren that there is no one or no thing to love must deliberately search for a love object. As a temporary, quick, and interim solution, one can utilize art objects, plants, pets, or other available nonhuman objects. But this should never become a permanent solution to the exclusion of human love. Life is not fulfilled without human love, and the search for it must go on. Here, also, one can utilize temporary objects. Love and service for one's doctor, pastor, nurse, or fellow patients may be sustaining temporarily until a more appropriate and lasting relationship can be established. Love and service are linked, and through service it is possible at times to find love. A commitment can be made to certain work in one's family or community, in one's sickroom, or with certain acquaintances. This commitment can grow into a sustaining relationship. The effort to find love can tax one's ingenuity, but the knowledge that only thus can life be fulfilled will help in the search that must be made.

The Meaning of One's Suffering

Whenever illness is discussed in a religious framework, one must ask if any meaning can be found in one's suffering. Gibran, in his book *The Wanderer*,[12] tells the story of one oyster who spoke to a neighboring oyster, "I have a very great pain within me. It is heavy and round and I am in distress." And the other oyster replied with haughty complacency, "Praise be to the heavens and to the sea, I have no pain within me. I am well and

[12] Kahlil Gibran, *The Wanderer* (New York: Alfred A. Knopf, 1932).

whole both within and without." At that moment a crab was passing by and heard the two oysters, and he said to the one who was well and whole within and without, "Yes, you are well and whole; but the pain that your neighbor bears is a pearl of exceeding beauty." Many patients with chronic illnesses have felt that there is a design, purpose, and reason behind their illnesses. They can answer, at least to their own satisfaction, the question why they were thrust into the crucible of an illness. Perhaps with Thomas Jefferson, although he was speaking of war, those who were or are patients can also say: "We gratefully acknowledge and signal instances of the Divine factor toward us, that His providence would not permit us to be called into this severe controversy until we had grown up to our present strength . . . and possessed of the means of protecting ourselves."

The religious person often expects health and happiness to be a by-product of his commitment to God. God does demand a total commitment, but he promises neither health nor happiness. The patient who embraces religion in order to obtain relief from his illness will almost invariably be doomed to disappointment. When one positively seeks his own health, he is encumbered by an increased self-awareness and self-consciousness which serve only to perpetuate and enhance his symptoms. In matters of health, as well as in other spheres, no greater wisdom was ever given man than the admonition that "he who would save his life shall lose it," and "he who would lose his life will find it."

Thus, in the biblical tradition, the forgetting of self, the cultivation of attitudes of love and service, creates the condition out of which health may evolve, for health is one of the facets of wholeness and harmony. It is significant that the biblical reference is to the sick man being made whole. The story certainly implies that if one is sick, there is a flaw within him impeding him from reacting peacefully and as a whole to the stresses of his environment and to their reverberations within him.

Christianity has always been concerned with bodily and mental health and has sought the relief of human suffering. But health is not the supreme good at any time, nor is one's present experience of disease, physical or mental, necessarily an indication of a personal fall from grace. Neither is health necessarily an indication of a state of grace. Because health, theologically speaking, is a relative good, it may become the focus for idolatry. Williams, while affirming the biblical concern for health, including physical well-being, reminds us:

The Christian ideal of life envisions something higher than freedom from anguish, or invulnerability to its ravages. Its goals cannot be the perfectly adjusted self. In the world as it is, a caring love cannot but regard such a goal as intolerably self-centered. What does it mean to be completely adjusted and at peace in a world as riddled with injustice, with the cries of the hungry, with the great unsolved questions of human living as this? We see why in the end we cannot identify therapy for specific ills with salvation for the human spirit. To live in love means to accept the risks of life and its threats to "peace in mind." Certainly the Christian ministry to persons is concerned to relieve physical ills, anxieties, inner conflicts. But this relief of private burdens is to set the person free to assume more important and universal ones.[13]

Similarly, Wayne Oates warns against a "religion that shapes itself around human needs rather than calling for a transformation of human nature into a new creation." [14]

Maybe the key to our health rests to a great extent in our relationship to God and to our fellow human beings. Through our relationships our love blossoms, the self is forgotten, and a sense of community and oneness with all mankind is found.

---

[13] Daniel D. Williams, *The Minister and the Care of Souls* (New York: Harper & Bros., 1961), pp. 25-26.
[14] *The Religious Dimensions of Personality* (New York: Association Press, 1957), p. 26; cf. pp. 105-6.

12
The Care of the Dying

The clergyman and the physician must understand and appreciate each other's work and relationships with the dying. Both have specific responsibilities and enter into major decisions regarding the physical, psychological, and spiritual welfare of the patient.

Often there is lack of communication between the two. This is especially true concerning what should or should not be told the patient about his condition. The physician usually makes the decision as to what information is given a patient and expects everybody else to hold to this decision. Yet often his decision is not known, for he has not bothered to share it with other members of the healing team. This places the clergyman in a difficult situation, because he does not know what is to be told. The patient turns to him in the spirit of truth and honesty, but the clergyman is forced to work in a setting where depth in understanding and communication can hardly be attained. It is good practice for the physician, clergyman, and nurse, as well as members of the family, to make decisions together as to how information should be handled with the patient. The physician usually welcomes help with this task, and once he has had experience in sharing this decision with the pastor, he would not want to follow any other approach.

Certain ethical and philosophic implications involved in the care of dying patients are causing physicians some genuine soul-searching. They need help from the church to guide them in many of these matters. Although part of this chapter may seem to be addressed primarily to the physician, the pastor who knows the sickroom will be no stranger to the issues raised here. It is hoped that the clergyman will see how close to his own concerns are many of the fears, paradoxes, and dilemmas of the physician. When each understands the work of the other and seeks to help the other in his work with the patient, then the patient finds the ministry he needs as he enters upon the "great threshold."

Ethical standards are not acquired by repeating the Oath of Hippocrates or the Prayer of Maimonides, nor is a moral sense developed by osmosis alone on the hospital wards. The physician ought to acquaint himself with the discussions of social scientists and philosophers. He must hold to his Hippocratic oath, but in the light of present-day knowledge and his own spiritual values. He needs the clergyman as a member of the healing team not only to minister to the patient but also to the physician.

The experience of taking care of patients during their final days and of deciding how they should be managed often furnishes the impetus for introspection and soul-searching. One finds himself in philosophic discussions with his colleagues. He avoids certain aspects of the problem of terminal care and faces others. He is fortunate if he has a clergyman colleague with whom he can discuss his concerns.

During my youth I often heard my parents speak of the final words spoken by some dying relative, friend, or neighbor. These people died with dignity, and memories of the final scene were treasured by those who witnessed it.

Another strong recollection is that of the biblical stories of the patriarchs who in dying encompassed their deaths with such dignity and meaning that all present felt a part of all mankind.

In the modern hospitals of today—beautiful and factory-like in efficiency—I have rarely seen a patient die in peace. The family is displaced from the room to make space available for all the machines which will take over bodily functions. Tubes are in every orifice of the patient's body, and intravenous fluids are running into one or more veins. As the patient dies, a series of heroic medical acts are performed which often result only in prolonging the act of dying.

Why is the medical profession caught up in such a fruitless struggle? This is an important area for the church to help the physician find the proper perspective in the care of the terminal patient.

We must train those who attend the dying in the art of using those procedures which best relieve and comfort the patient that he may go his way with dignity and with a cherished memory left behind to sustain and ennoble the lives of those who follow.

Let me emphasize that neither I nor any other physician would ever advocate taking a positive step to hasten the end of a patient who is suffering. When our assessment of the situation clearly points to the fact that in our judgment the patient is going to die, then we may soften our efforts to heal the patient physically and increase our efforts to support and comfort him. In such a situation we are bringing to the forefront a dimension which has long been a part of medicine—to comfort always.

At this stage in the physician's new relationship with the patient, he should no longer let the medical equipment in the room stand as a barrier between the patient and his relatives. The patient is entitled to dignity in death.

If the doctor and pastor help to draw the patient and his family closer together, the act of dying becomes a more sacred moment. The doctor himself should see that the situation is such that the pastor can fulfill his responsibilities to patient and family.

Prolonging Life or the Act of Dying

After George Washington, dying of edema of the larynx, had suffered repeated bleedings, purgings, and blisterings—then current methods of scientific medicine—he implored his persecutors: "I pray you to take no more trouble for me. Let me go quietly."

George Washington's physicians were diligent to the end because in his case they thought they were prolonging life, when actually they were prolonging the act of dying. With our modern scientific skills and drugs we can prolong the act of dying to frightening lengths. Often we hear statements today, usually regarding the elderly, that science will not let people die naturally, even when they are ready and longing for death. This attitude is often considered respect for life, but one wonders if it is not, in the words of Martin Buber, "man's lust for whittling away the secret of death." The good physician trains himself to prolong life, but not to prolong the act of dying. The terrifying dilemma which often confronts him is, "Which am I doing?"

If it has been established beyond any doubt that the patient is *in extremis*, if the physician and his associates are in unanimous agreement, and if there is no question in anyone's mind about the prognosis, are extraordinary measures indicated to keep the patient alive a little longer? Only rarely would the patient's wish be known in this matter. Usually the relatives would not want to prolong the act of dying. No voices representative of the Roman Catholic or Greek Orthdox Churches or of the Jewish or Protestant faiths have suggested that physicians should try extraordinary means to keep life going when every process of the body is determined to die. His Holiness, Pope Pius XII, issued an encyclical during the last year of his life which stated the official position of the Roman Catholic Church as not requiring extraordinary means when only suffering and certain death lie ahead.

In spite of much thought and discussion on the subject of terminal care the doctor remains troubled by the elderly or hopelessly ill patient who longs for death as an end to his suffering. Shall we try to ease his symptoms as he goes, or shall we force him to suffer yet a little while longer, because science has given us such things as "miracle drugs" and machines which can take over the function of certain organs of the body? "Lord, now lettest thou thy servant depart in peace, according to thy word" we read in the Gospel of St. Luke, the beloved physician. These words should both guide and comfort us.

The Tendency to Withdraw from the Dying

An experience during my Junior year in medical school dramatically brought to my attention the tendency to withdraw from a dying patient. One of my classmates was assigned to take care of a thirty-year-old white man with leukemia. Our clinical group of three students knew this patient and his wife, and participated in his care for the three months he was in the hospital prior to his death.

For two and a half months we (the students) continued to be hopeful about the patient's recovery. Then one complication after another befell the patient, and we came to realize that he was beginning slowly to die. The two of us who were not responsible for his care began to stay away from his bedside, whereas previously we had been regular attendants in his room, mostly for conversation with him and his wife. We were hardly aware that we were staying away. One day I met his wife in the hall, and she asked, "Why don't you come to visit us any more?" At a loss for words, I finally muttered, "Well, since we can't do anything, we would only be in the way." She replied, "Oh, no; he misses you. He knows he is not going to live and that medication will not help him, but both he and I want to share with you our thoughts and feelings in this crisis. You could be of great help to us." This experience gave our group an opportunity to explore with the staff several crucial factors in the care of terminal patients.

In the first place, one must never overlook the fact that he, himself, can be an instrument of therapy. Mankind has known from the beginning of time that healing and comfort come from human relationships. Both the physician and the pastor forget this sometimes in today's emphasis on drugs and surgical procedures.

Second, why did we stay away? Two of us could rationalize that we were not responsible for the patient's care, but both he and his wife looked upon all three of us as active in the treatment process. Possibly we stayed away because of our anxiety about death. Many medical students, physicians, and clergymen have not worked through their own feelings about death and the finiteness of their own lives. Thus, they cannot be comfortable with a patient as he approaches death. Guilt feelings must also be reckoned with. On some level of awareness we realized that a man was dying while we were allowed to live. Why? This question is asked repeatedly by most who care for the dying. Another major possibility was that this death was an attack on our "fantasied omnipotence." We were losing a battle with death, and we felt impotent. Death had been presented by our instructors as the great enemy. When a fight with death is lost, the physician is confronted by feelings of inadequacy as a healer. The clergyman often shares these feelings.

Our instructors insisted that regardless of how we feel, we should never abandon the dying patient, especially if we are at all responsible for his care. We must be willing to discuss with him any concerns which may be brought up in those final days. Walt Whitman challenges us through his words: "The faithful hand of the living does not desert the hand of the dying."

The dying patient experiences a penetrating type of loneliness and aloneness. He needs a shoulder to lean on as he becomes oriented to his new situation and works out some kind of solution to his approaching fate. The family also has its burdens. If physician, clergyman, family, and friends form a true community of spirit with the dying patient, the feelings of isolation and separation accompanying death are neutralized or minimized.

Such was the situation with a five-year-old boy whom I knew well while serving as a house physician on the Children's Service at Duke University Hospital. He suspected from the tragic expression on the faces of his parents that he was going to die. He asked one of his doctors if this were the case. His doctor told him honestly that he was very sick and that so far the treatment had not been very effective. He asked the boy gently if he were afraid, and the boy returned the question. They both decided that they were not. The following day when the boy's parents visited him, he told them that everything would be all right regardless of what happened, and that they should not worry. They asked, "Why do you feel that way?" His simple and moving reply was, "Because my doctors love me."

Sensitive Response to the Dying

The terminally ill patient often has an unconscious fear of being "untouchable." The touch or caress is the most basic nonverbal comforting technique we possess, and it communicates a solace to the disturbed or frightened patient that words can never produce. Thus, the routine backrub or massage given by the nurse engenders both physical and psychic well-being. The clergyman places his hands upon the patient in prayer. The physician examines with his hands the part of the body in pain. These are all ministries which the dying patient desperately needs.

No patient should ever be treated as if he had no future. Even though a patient is terminal, he should be encouraged to plan for himself and his family, particularly his children. Children are living defenses against the fear of being blotted out, and terminally ill patients can derive comfort and satisfaction from the visits of their children and from helping them plan their future.

Many feel that to neglect the question of whether the patient is dying often causes his sense of alienation and profound loneliness to increase. Patients usually feel alienated from the family which is not telling them the truth—a truth that they suspect. Leo Tolstoi understood this and wrote, in *The Death of Ivan Ilyich:* "What tormented Ivan Ilyich most was the deception—their not wishing to admit what they all knew and what he knew, but wanting to lie to him, and forcing him to participate in that lie. . . . And he had thus to live all alone on the brink of an abyss, with no one who understood or pitied him."

Closeness and warmth are helpful remedies in the lonely business of dying. Thus it is usually in the best interest of the patient that he know his condition, and I advocate truth as the approach in dealing with the patient. This does not mean that the patient must be told bluntly that he has a fatal or incurable disease. The truth should be so presented that it does not cut off a source of hope. Hope for improvement is never lost, even when a cure is impossible. Truth and hope are not mutually exclusive.

The road of truth is not always the easiest road to follow in ministering to the dying, but it is the road which can lead to fruitful encounter and a sense of community in the life of the patient. Such a course of action demands an attitude of sensitive response on the part of the physician and clergyman, of entering into the feelings of the patient rather than avoiding or directing them.

Therapeutically, one aspect of our work with the dying patient relates to his grief reaction. The loss or threat of loss of a loved one will precipitate grief, no matter how implicit the faith in a later reunion. While the relative of the dying man stands to lose the affection and companionship of a single loved one, the dying man stands to lose the affection and companionship of everyone. Also he relinquishes his work, his possessions, and, if he has children, his chance to see them grow up. Thus his grief is infinitely more severe and overwhelming. It is not surprising that he has greater need to protect himself by using mechanisms such as denial. Possibly those of us who counsel the dying patient may well take into consideration this grief reaction both on the part of the patient and his family and work with it in a manner similar to the way we work with the grief reaction in a different circumstance.

Those who have worked with children in terminal illness have noticed that children generally accept, without obvious panic, the restrictions imposed on them as the disease progresses. They have less interest in their surroundings as their energy diminishes. Children often ask if their illness is not their fault and punishment for something they did. They must be reassured that such is not the case.

The family's reaction to the prospective death of the child can be compared to separation anxiety. The normal process of mourning usually occurs before the child dies. The family must be allowed this period of mourning, which involves a concentration of interest and energies, self-examination, self-condemnation, and guilt. Parents need to go through these processes, and they need their pastor's and physician's permission to do so. The pastor and physician can permit them to voice their guilt and assure them by the gentle and understanding manner in which they answer their questions. Questions frequently asked are: Should I have called the doctor sooner? Did the child inherit the disease from one of us? Did the injury he received some time ago contribute to this illness? Do you think my spanking him may have brought this on? Intellectually, most parents know that these doubts are unreasonable, but they ask such questions because they are so deeply involved emotionally. Ventilation of their anxieties and the pastor's and physician's reassurances ease their discomfort.

When the parents' guilt has been worked through, their energies should be redirected. The physician and the pastor are both in strategic positions to help in this redirection by guiding them back to the rest of the family. Some parents become active in organizations dedicated toward the study and eradication of certain diseases.

Conclusion

We must ever remind ourselves of the dignity and profundity often attained by an individual in his final hours. Such a reminder is contained in a letter from a soldier to his wife, written in the last hours of the battle of Stalingrad, knowing he would not survive:

It is strange that people value things only when they are about to lose them. The vast distance is spanned by the bridge from heart to heart. . . . As long as there are shores, there will always be bridges. We should have the courage to walk on them. One bridge leads to you, the other to eternity; at the very end they are the same for me. Tomorrow I shall set forth on the last bridge; give me your hand, so that crossing it won't be so hard.[1]

[1] Quoted in the Chicago *Daily Tribune*, October 7, 1961.

13

The Psychiatrist in
the Life and Work of the Church

The concept of the priesthood of all believers places a very special mantle of responsibility and opportunity upon the shoulders of a scientist working in the field of human behavior. On the professional road which he travels he walks with those in bondage and liberation, exile and homecoming, oppression and deliverance.

It is the misfortune of our age that we insist on fragmenting man and his activity into the secular and the religious. In spite of the great Hebraic tradition with its marvelous statements and teachings about the body, so beautifully illustrated in the Old Testament, many religious people today almost deny the existence of the biological. The psychiatrist is forced by his work to view man in broad perspective. In the research or treatment situation, although he is aware of the somatic, psychic, and spiritual dimensions of human life, he is working for wholeness in the individual. In health the dimensions are so interlocked that only man in his totality is seen. Thus the psychiatrist has a vocation which deals with the totality of man, with man as a unit.

A Unitary Approach to Man

Present-day psychiatry has made it impossible to think in terms of a dualistic approach to health and illness but rather has considered it essential that health and illness be seen in such a way that body, mind, and spirit, as well as interpersonal relationships, are all involved at all times. Thus, religion can never be attacked as being irrelevant to health and illness.

The message in the Gospels discloses that an intimate relationship was taken for granted between physical, mental, moral, and religious health. Incidents are recorded in which a physical affliction was healed and sins were forgiven in one and the same act. The various needs of the sick individual were seen to be manifestations of a single need—a need for wholeness. Nobody attempted to split human health into a multiplicity of functions, and likewise nobody attempted to promote the welfare of one individual in abstraction from the salvation of the community. Each person saw and felt the spirit of God working through the religious community and knew himself to be a part of the priesthood of all believers.

Psychiatry has pointed out to certain of the medical specialities that humanity cannot capitalize upon medicine's scientific efforts unless these efforts can be used in the service of personal and social integration. If modern medical skills restore a man to physical fitness and he continues to suffer from emptiness and anxiety, the physical fitness may be relatively futile or the physical recovery may actually be short-lived.

Psychiatry may also be credited with having asserted that many of the assets of specialization are lost if each scientific discipline goes off in its individual direction and at the same time produces presuppositions in conflict with those of other disciplines. Thus any type of dualism or fragmentation is out of date unless it is only a means to increase the detail and exactitude of our understanding about the total man.

Psychiatry has led the church away from the old concept of considering the inner life of man sacrosanct and untouchable, and has encouraged exploration and analysis of man's inner life. Through such efforts, at least potentially, some new light has been shed on the criteria of sin and salvation. As has been frequently pointed out a salvation which leads a person into outward conformity to some pattern but betrays him into illness by repressing inner problems is a poor type of salvation.

It is good that many psychiatrists and psychologists, such as Viktor Frankl, A. H. Maslow, and Gordon Allport, are stressing man's search for meaning as a much stronger drive than man's search for pleasure or for power. And all of us in this field can attest to the number of patients we see who are complaining less about specific symptoms than they are about a feeling of inner emptiness, of absence of purpose, of lack of direction. To concentrate on relieving these symptoms through uncovering their origin in the past or to seek to reveal the extent to which they operate in a person's life in the present, would be only a partly effective therapeutic procedure. A focus on meaning reorients the patient toward his life task with the consequence that the symptom becomes an unimportant detail. Symptoms, then, are dealt with as indications of failure to measure up to the responsibility of undertaking one's personal mission in life.

The Vocatio Dei

Neither man nor the life he lives can rightly be broken into segments. Certain experiences cannot be called secular and others religious. Religion can and should pervade all of life. It is a calling forth of all of man's capacities and skills into worship and work for the common good of all, by a power greater than himself or the world in which he lives.

The monastic ideal of the medieval church commended the lives of celibate clergy and the religious as more pleasing to God than the lives of the common people engaged in doing the ordinary work of the world. Certain medieval preachers and mystics, however, applied to these common pursuits an impressive term—Vocatio Dei, "divine calling." Luther and Calvin followed and overpassed the lead of these preachers and mystics. The reformers declared that what a man can do with his hands and brain is not within itself pleasing to God, but that all God requires of any man—faith and obedience—can be shown by each person in that place to which the divine will has assigned him. Luther, Calvin, and their like-minded contemporaries set the example for a genuinely new estimate of everyday life and toil. It was a fresh approach toward reassertion of the ancient premise that worship and ordinary work belong together, that the adoration of God should be integral to everyday life.

This concept of vocation is emphasized in order to show that the psychiatrist's vocation, as well as all others, implies a call. The question immediately asked is, Called by whom and to what? The call is from God and it is a call to life. It is high time that the leaders in the church abandon the use of such misleading terms as "secular psychiatrists" or "secular behavioral scientists." Recently I heard a prominent clergyman use these terms in a sermon in which he poked fun at the efforts of these individuals to bring to people a peace that "bypasseth" all understanding. While the professionals in the psychiatric and psychological disciplines, as well as patients with emotional disorders, listen to such references in sermons, they feel more lonely than ever and more acutely aware of how great is the harvest field of disordered human behavior, how few are the skilled laborers, and how inadequate are the tools and methods to gather this harvest. Why cannot the church seek out rather than alienate the psychiatrist? He is called of God to a life of faith and obedience within the framework of his own discipline. His concerns are not removed from the concerns of the church. He, too, wrestles with the predicament of modern man. In discussion and in clinical practice he has to deal with anxiety, death, the overcoming of man's separateness, the conflict between the counterfeit and the genuine self, the faceless man of the masses, freedom, and love.

A Participant in Healing

A special area of concern has been the "hearing of confessions and forgiving of sins" by those in psychiatry. If we take seriously the doctrine of the priesthood of all believers, then the priestly work of bringing divine forgiveness to overburdened consciences and peace to despairing souls is a work which God delegates not only to the official clergy of the church but to every individual Christian. There should be trained father-confessors to pronounce priestly absolution in the name of Christ and the church, but it is good that many laymen are able to do a similar thing very effectively, simply by receiving wrongdoers into fellowship and declaring God's mercy to them as much by attitude as by speech. Years ago I read a story of a lay person's part in priestly absolution which I have remembered through the years.

A young woman was brought into a hospital after she had been stabbed in a drunken brawl in a disreputable section of the city. All medical care possible was given her, but the case was hopeless. A nurse was asked to sit by the unconscious girl until death came. As the nurse sat looking at the coarse lines on a face so young, the girl opened her eyes and spoke: "I want you to tell me something and tell me straight. Do you think God cares about people like me? Do you think he could forgive anyone as bad as me?" The nurse was hesitant to reply until she had reached out to God for a kind of authorization and reached out toward the injured girl with a feeling of oneness with her. Then, knowing that she spoke in truth, she said: "I am telling you straight. God cares about you, and he forgives you." The girl gave a sigh of relief and slipped back into unconsciousness, and, as she died, the coarse lines disappeared from her face. Something momentous happened between God and that girl through the nurse.[1]

Among those whom the church designates as laymen probably none have more opportunities than psychiatrists to be ministers of the grace of God. The psychiatrist may be an instrument of God's grace both in his work with the individual and with society. He may receive God's message and interpret it in a meaningful way for himself, for other individuals, and for society in general. Berdyaev emphasized God's way of working in our world:

Divine revelation is communicated to the world and acts in it through man. Man passionately longs to hear the voice of God, but he can only hear it in and through himself. Man is the mediator between God and himself. God always spoke through man—through Moses, through the prophets, through the great sages, the apostles, the Fathers of the Church, the saints. The only way to God is through man. Man carries within himself the divine principle, the

[1] Walter M. Horton, *Our Eternal Contemporary* (New York: Harper & Bros., 1942), pp. 82-84.

word of God. And as a free being he carries it creatively and actively and not passively and receptively. God expresses Himself in the world through interaction with man, through meeting man, through man's answering His call, through the refraction of the divine principle in human freedom. Hence the extraordinary complexity of the religious life.[2]

The psychiatrist through his empirical studies may give us a clearer understanding of the nature of man, his shadow side, and his cry for redemption. Probably no professional group has taken more seriously the admonition of Carl Jung to wander with human heart through the world to study man in all the situations of life in which he could be involved. Jung encouraged those who wanted to learn how to doctor the sick with real knowledge of the human soul to visit mental and general hospitals, suburban pubs, gambling halls, brothels, places of business, revival meetings, etc.

When man is seen and studied in this context, one recognizes immediately the relevance of the gospel as concerned not so much with teaching us how to solve such problems but with healing and regenerating the texture of the inner life of man. It is the task of man, and in a special sense the psychiatrist, in his freedom, to find a creative solution for the problems that continually confront him in his life in society.

Acceptance

The psychiatrist, in his psychotherapeutic role, has reemphasized for the church the profound relevance of its message of acceptance. Paul Tillich has stressed in many of his writings how the church's doctrine of divine acceptance, traditionally called the doctrine of "justification by grace through faith," has been buried under doctrinal rigidity and aridity. The doctrine is meant to communicate to man the good news that he who feels unworthy of being accepted by God can be certain that he is accepted. The pattern in psychotherapy of a nonjudging and nondirecting acceptance of the emotionally disturbed has had an

[2] Nicolas Berdyaev, *The Destiny of Man* (New York: Harper & Row, 1960), pp. 53-54.

influence both on pastoral counseling and theological inquiry.

Because of this nonjudgmental attitude, the psychiatrist is often rightly accused of permissiveness. However, this permissiveness is often wrongly confused with moral indifference. In reality, the problem has arisen because the psychiatrist has insisted that one's moral problem will be solved not by restricting and restraining the unknown impulses of one's depths but by allowing these to break through and be constructively utilized. Carl Jung always emphasized that man should accept his shadow or dark side and come to grips with it or else become a victim of seriously disordered behavior. When Jung spoke about mature morality, he did not view this as a torturous and impossible obedience to any external standards, whether they be cultural and religious codes or personal ideals. He emphasized that true morality emerges through one's own nature, as he is made increasingly aware of his own depths and of the extension of these depths beyond himself.

Other psychiatrists would be in complete agreement with Jung on this point, and see the meaning of neurosis as often having a relationship to a moral problem. The relationship here would exist in the sense that an individual gradually develops a rather rigid "conscious" moral image of himself, related to parental, religious, or cultural standards. Then, in the light of this image, he refuses to recognize the demands, impulses, or potentialities of his shadow or contradictory side. The refusal to recognize this other side and come to grips with it naturally leads to internal conflict or self-division, which for Jung constituted the essence of neurosis. Paul understood this situation and wrote: "For the good that I would I do not: but the evil which I would not, that I do" (Rom. 7:19).

This discussion has focused on the person whose moral image of himself is good. Thus the conflict arises because the conscious mind hangs on to its moral ideal while the unconscious strives after the immoral or bad ideal which the conscious mind tries to deny. At this point Jung went further than Freud and came to the realization that one often has a conscious image of himself as *bad* or worthless. In such a case the good or worthy side is unacceptable and must be kept hidden as the unacknowledged shadow. Thus the conflict is reversed. A man may appear in every way disreputable and this turns out to be only a pose of wickedness, for he has hidden his moral side which has fallen into the unconscious.

Psychiatrists have been quick to recognize the possibility of movement into consciousness or unconsciousness of either the good or the shadow side of man. Thus, acceptance of the patient and urging that the patient accept himself introduced inadvertently into the mind of the public questions about moral permissiveness.

The therapist, in helping the patient to accept himself in the situation of guilt, does not do therapy by suspending judgment. The ancient biblical principle that the law condemns and destroys if it is not preceded by forgiveness often seems more widely accepted in psychotherapy circles than in certain theological ones. Patients will feel it if there is even a trace of condemnation, though never formulated, in the depths of the therapist's mind. If such condemnation exists the therapeutic relationship is destroyed. At no place does the saving power of charity become more apparent. Often the patient, consciously or unconsciously, wants to be condemned. This may not be a healthy desire for moral restitution but an infantile seeking of punishment. Patients not infrequently tell startling stories of antisocial or immoral behavior, expecting to be preached at or given a moral beating. The frustration of a patient's desire for punishment, rejection, or condemnation within the psychotherapeutic situation often contributes to his moral regeneration. This is the great paradox of effective therapy. The good pastor, as well as the psychotherapist, has always known that the deepest guilt feeling always comes from the message of grace and not from the proclamation of the law. In the world of the gospel guilt is not deadweight but building material. In that context the problem of guilt is the problem of love. One of the thieves who was crucified with Jesus did not indulge in lengthy self-accusations. He performed a simple act of love, and he was answered: "Today shalt thou be with me in paradise" (Luke 23:43). And of the sinful woman who kissed and anointed Jesus' feet, these words were spoken: "Her sins, which are many, are forgiven; for she loved much" (Luke 7:47). In both the thief and the sinful woman, through the transcendence of love, there was no anxiety or struggle for self-assertion, for in the relatedness to Christ the self was received as a gift of grace.

Symbols

The psychiatrist may help the church discover the lost meaning of its symbols. Martin Buber has said that there are epochs when the symbols are empty of God's spirit. Man today seems cut off from the depths of his unconscious mind, from whence sustenance and healing could come. Carl Jung often expressed his concern that Christianity had become a religion of consciousness. Thus the followers of the Christian faith were cut off from their unconscious. The symbols and rites through which our faith has traditionally been expressed do not communicate the revelation of what is divine, or bring the healing they once did to the divided person. Our rationalistic, scientific approach to religion, with an accompanying intellectualization of all religious matters, has closed for us the door of understanding regarding symbols. They no longer speak to us or guide, revive, or heal us.

The psychotherapeutic disciplines are working to resuscitate the deeper levels of man's being. For centuries the symbols, rites, and myths of the faith opened for man the gates of reality and spoke to him in meaningful richness from the depths of his being. If symbolic communication in the religious realm is again established, it is hoped that psychiatrists will have had their part in bringing this to pass.

A Divine Framework

The psychiatrist who is committed to the church brings within the scope of his work a divine framework and perspective. The old classic Dutch and Italian paintings of a room within a home usually portrayed an open window through which one could see a lake, gardens, or forest. This artistic practice contrasts sharply with a rigidly and narrowly focused technique, illustrated in the painting of Whistler's Mother. The religious and the nonreligious approaches closely parallel these artistic techniques in that the former includes the extra dimension of the ultimate. Although both may accept the famous statement which guided Jung's life: *Vocatus atque non vocatus Deus aberit* (Invited, even not invited, God is present), the recognition and acknowledgment of his presence may permit his influence to be more easily felt and heeded.

Values

Another way in which the psychiatrist may express his commitment is by adding to his growing technical competence a broader and deeper realization of life's persistent ethical problems. Because psychotherapy affects the values which determine life's choices, almost every kind of moral issue emerges during treatment. The therapist cannot console himself that his form of treatment is purely technical and that he need take no stand on moral issues. Although an individual may not dictate another's choice nor may he stand aloof, the therapist finds a wide range between these two extremes. The therapist can raise relevant questions about which the patient has not thought and supply pertinent information. His own wisdom and insights enter the picture. He participates in healing with what he himself is, as well as with his studied arts. His character arises both from his knowledge and his experience. Although the therapist may deny giving his patient any value system, the patient seems to learn rather quickly the therapist's values and very often incorporates them. The most pronounced failure of modern psychotherapy is its inability to handle the total person. It does a superb job of analyzing the problem but falters when it tries to go further. Is it because psychotherapy is often so oriented toward digging into the past for the forgotten or for the dead? Are present goals or the impingement of the future not given enough weight? Has not the oft-used psychotherapeutic approach been so reductionistic that every good work, every deed, and every thought are reduced to some infantile act of the past?

Erich Fromm has stressed repeatedly in his writings the conviction that our civilization relentlessly and systematically crushes and corrupts man's deepest needs and noblest powers. At the heart of all his researches there is a compelling sorrow and a unifying vision. His sorrow is for man, chained, isolated and suffering. His vision is of men freed, with wounds healed, restored to strength—man in the image of God. Psychiatrists should join Fromm and stand in judgment of our society, which by its present structure seeks to corrode and distort the *Imago Dei* in man.

The psychiatrist should insist that no science dealing with man can be divorced from problems of philosophy and ethics. He should insist that percepts without ethical concepts are blind and impotent, not merely to understand the world but to change it.

Within the structure of human personality and of society moral values have a reality of their own. These moral values are as real as sexual drives, aggression, and love. It is a strange paradox that, at this time, when the inroads of psychiatry have begun to offer new and dramatic insights into human nature, the social and cultural dimensions of morality have become increasingly blurred and blunted. As a deeply religious psychiatrist pointed out recently, the psychiatrist cannot be entirely blamed if he shares in the numbness and confusion of a civilization which requires acts of murder and violence to reach overwhelming, catastrophic proportions before allowing itself to respond with shock and sadness. However, because of the psychiatrist's special knowledge and experience, he bears a particular responsibility to be more aware than he is of the impact of such a state of affairs on himself, and in turn, on his patients.

The psychiatrist possibly sees more clearly than others the place hostility is holding within the economy of our life. The anxiety which seems to characterize our age may be, in part, a response or reactive awareness that one is surrounded by a hostile world and threatened from within by internal hostilities. Freud wrote of man's aggressive and destructive drives as forces of death (Thanatos). In his discussion of the death instinct, Freud states that the tendency toward destruction and aggression is an innate and independent instinctual disposition in man, and that it constitutes the most powerful obstacle to culture. While one may not accept Freud's concept in its biological orientation, he may accept it on an ontological basis and see hostility, aggression, and destructiveness as inevitable, basic, and structural.

Destructiveness of attitude and behavior is nurtured and strengthened during the course of faulty upbringing of a child in his family and through influences in his neighborhood. The psychiatrist can rethink his position on the causes of crime, delinquency, and other forms of antisocial behavior and question the assumption of relating antisocial behavior mostly to mental illness or extremes of poverty, rather than to the absence of, or to faulty, value education. If religious, social, and moral values are not presented to children in their formative years, then they most likely will lack them.

Conscience is recognized by most authorities as representing inner controls. Although the capacity for conscience is innate, and there are dimensions of conscience that extend beyond mere socialization, much of the content and application of conscience come from the family and society. Thus, the child needs to be introduced to the higher value system of the group in which he is living. Where instruction is not given, or where the family and society have become uncertain of basic values and consequently have developed a collective instability and uncertainty about values, one sees a developmental defect in the spiritual and moral dimension of man.

Conclusion

In the people of Israel, and from the days of Jesus' preaching down to the present, the church has never separated its message of salvation from its concern for concrete service to human beings—healing their sickness, meeting their needs—as it offers to all men a new life of faith in God.

At present psychiatry brings a new set of challenges and possibilities to the church. Among these is the requirement that the church look again at the nature and dynamics of human emotional life. The discovery of new healing powers and methods for dealing with human ills has provided resources which the church must respect and use in its ministry to human beings. For many in our culture the psychological exploration of the human soul with its mysteries has been the route by which they have been led back to a deeper appreciation of the central concepts of the biblical faith. Anton Boisen has stressed for years that psychological crisis and illness may have religious meaning.[3] Gotthard Booth, as a psychiatrist, has written on the spiritual significance of illness.[4] Therefore, doctrines and symbols of Christianity, such as grace, forgiveness, wrath of God, and resurrection may become available to those who have lost the sense of their meaning.

The psychiatrist has been given special status in our society and is usually accepted and highly respected. With these privileges go responsibilities. The ideas and ideals which should guide his life could scarcely be more pungently expressed than in a prayer written by Augustine:

O Lord, our Saviour, who hast warned us that Thou wilt require much of those to whom much is given; Grant that we, whose lot is cast in so goodly a heritage, may strive together the more abundantly to extend to others what we so richly enjoy. And as we have entered into the labours of other men, so to labour, that, in turn, other men may enter into ours, to the fulfillment of Thy holy will.

---

[3] The Exploration of the Inner World (New York: Harper & Bros., 1952).
[4] "Healing the Sick," Pastoral Psychology, June, 1962, pp. 11-24.

INDEX

203